AJC Press
6400 Oak Canyon, Suite 200
Irvine, CA 92618

ISBN: 978-0-692-78111-1

Publisher's Cataloging-in-Publication Data

New Possibilities in Memory Care : The Silverado Story. Loren Shook and Stephen Winner. -- 2nd ed. -- Irvine, CA : AJC Press, c2017

ISBN: 978-0-692-78111-1

Dusk jacket, book design and cover photography: Frédéric Tiberghien

This book is intended for your enjoyment and general education only. This is not an authoritative medical manual, though this publication is designed to provide accurate and important information regarding the subject matter. Everyone is a unique individual with their own specific medical history and needs, so if professional medical advice or other expert assistance is required regarding any of the matters covered in this book, the services of a professional should be sought.

Printed in the United States of America.

PRAISE

Loren Shook and Stephen Winner show us that memory impairment doesn't have to mean the end of life. At Silverado, it means a new stage of life based on love not fear. By replacing restraints, drugs and sterile surroundings with a cozy home, clubs, animals, and children, the "Silverado Way" makes it possible for people with cognitive impairments to live full, engaged lives again, with dignity and purpose. This story is an inspiration – simple but revolutionary. Millions will benefit if this incredibly humane vision becomes the norm.

Jeannine English
President, AARP (2012–2016)

In their book, Loren Shook and Steve Winner make the compelling argument that providing meaningful care to those with Alzheimer's and other memory-impairing diseases should rank alongside research into prevention and cure of the conditions as a top public priority. This is an important book and recommended reading for all who are concerned about the issue.

Frank M. LaFerla, Ph.D.
Chancellor's Professor and Chair,
Neurobiology and Behavior School of Biological Sciences
Director, Institute for Memory Impairments and Neurological Disorders
(UCI MIND), University of California, Irvine

The Silverado experience is such that each resident, (not patient), is treated with respect, dignity, and love. There are things beyond just being safe and living longer that are important. Every person my husband encountered was so caring and kind. There was support not only for my husband, but also for our entire family. We were still in his life, not just visitors to his life. When it came time for him to leave this earth, the entire staff surrounded us with support and love. He never had to go to a hospital, and died peacefully surrounded by the ones he loved. Who could ask for more?

Candy Pyle
Wife of Mike Pyle,
Captain of the 1963 NFL Champion Chicago Bears

In 1993 when my stepfather developed Parkinson's, we were unable to find a home that understood the needs of individuals with dementia. We settled on a community that was clean and safe but had no dementia experience. Three years later Loren Shook, Steve Winner and Jim Smith approached us about an entirely new concept – an assisted living that focused on improving quality of life for individuals with dementia. They had developed a care model that was focused on social interaction and participation, enabling the reduction of resident medication levels. Twenty years later, Silverado has brought life to tens of thousands of early- and late-stage dementia patients. Eventually, my mother developed Alzheimer's and spent the last two years of her life at Silverado where she was able to enjoy life again as she visited museums, music performances, and even a USC football practice. Even with an advanced illness, she was able to participate in life – all while her family knew she was safe and loved by the Silverado team.

J. Christopher Lewis
Riordan, Lewis & Haden Equity Partners
Silverado Board Member

This book puts into clear perspective why those of us involved in the field of human aging – from scientists to caregivers – do what we do. It truly is all about displaying compassionate understanding in the face of the great changes that come with older age and skillfully providing older adults with the environment and support that they need to maximize well-being in later life. Memory-impairment is one of the most difficult and heartrending challenges that can accompany aging, but Loren Shook and Steve Winner have shown us the importance of never letting our fears overwhelm our ability to provide loving care to those who need it most. Their story and their philosophy are an incredible inspiration to all of us who strive to make the world a better place for older adults.

Pinchas Cohen, M.D.
Dean, Leonard Davis School of Gerontology
Executive Director, Ethel Percy Andrus Gerontology Center
University of Southern California

This is a story of creating extraordinary results. Silverado is about living to our fullest, knowing "and" is more powerful than "or" – just as love is more powerful than fear. Any leader exploring how his or her organization can achieve more will find this easy-to-read story of innovation, courage and conviction to be inspiring and useful.

Vance Caesar, Ph.D.
Premier Leadership Coach
Business Visionary and Entrepreneur

Silverado is a story of innovation. More than five million people suffer from Alzheimer's and we must do everything possible to care for those who battle this terrible disease. Loren Shook and Steve Winner have demonstrated how a cutting-edge care model has the power to make a real difference in real lives. Not only has Silverado elevated the standard for memory care across the senior living industry, but they are also making an impact on health care overall with programs that improve cognitive and physical health and wellness. I am very proud of the partnership Welltower has built with Silverado to bring their innovative memory care program to more communities around the country, and build connectivity with health care systems to evolve the quality, efficiency and delivery of care for people as they age.

Thomas J. DeRosa
Chief Executive Officer and Director, Welltower

'The Silverado Story' leaves no doubt that love and compassion comprise the greatest means of touching the human spirit. Loren Shook and Steve Winner give a powerful testimony to the healing value of compassion and love, sharing touching examples of how lives are changed when fear is replaced by love in our everyday living.

W.E. (Bill) Sheriff
Retired CEO, Brookdale Senior Living

Loren Shook and Stephen Winner describe the philosophy and heart of the Silverado approach. The organization has developed a model for the care of the cognitively impaired that is being copied worldwide. It balances the needs for safety and independence in a way that is difficult to understand unless you see it yourself. The concept of community at Silverado is well described in this book and so are the motivations and approaches utilized by its leadership in the entire organization. This book is very useful reading for families of people with Alzheimer's and other dementias and for everyone caring for them.

Joe W. Ramsdell, M.D.
Division Head, General Internal Medicine
Professor of Clinical Medicine, Professor of Pulmonary
Director, Clinical Trials Center,
University of California, San Diego

I read 'The Silverado Story' with more than just casual interest. I have lived The Silverado Story. My beloved mother spent the last five years of her life at a Silverado community. I visited my mother nearly every day and saw the way in which Silverado took care of not just my mother, but all residents of her community. A different kind of care is provided – care a person will not find anywhere else. The stimulation residents receive; the respect they are shown by the staff; the love that is evident makes each visit to Silverado a special one. I loved my mother and I would not wish this disease on anyone. However, Silverado provided her, and just as importantly, our family, an environment during her final years that was worthy of her. It could not have been better.

Patrick C. Haden
Athletic Director (2010 – 2016)
University of Southern California

When my mother was diagnosed with Alzheimer's disease in her late seventies, it was a familiar situation. My father had died from complications with Alzheimer's a few years earlier. At this time, I was her primary caregiver, and one of the most painful aspects, among many, was her constant search for a purpose, a reason to go on. She kept saying, "I need a job." Of course, this was an impossibility and yet every time I could come up with a task for her to accomplish, her entire demeanor changed. She became energized, bright, and engaged. I felt that a program must be developed in communities dealing with dementia that would enable residents to feel motivated and purposeful. Loren Shook and Steve Winner identify an ideology that encompasses this concern and so many others. I am hopeful that this innovative book will impact senior care organizations everywhere.

Victor Garber
Film, Television and Stage Actor

There is often a "story behind the story". There are usually people whose lives create the story. But for the story to be worthwhile, there is always a burning passion inside those people whose dream is to make the world a better place. Loren Shook is that man. His vision, dream, and passion for helping those affected by memory impairment and his desire to care for them, their families and loved ones is evident in everything he does. Like Pastor Rick Warren who is mentioned in "The Silverado Story", Loren is a man who understands purpose and the power it unleashes. Loren has instilled a unique culture throughout the Silverado organization that is grounded in and supportive of their core operating philosophy of *Love is greater than fear*. The results are undeniable and the lives touched and improved speak for themselves. The Silverado story is not fully written yet...

Dave Arnold
Pastor – Strategic Initiatives
Saddleback Church
Lake Forest California

DEDICATIONS

From Loren

To my father and mother, Cleo and Kathleen Shook, who taught me the meaning of love, responsibility, a work ethic and values, and introduced me to the power of God, the spirit that lives within all of us.

To my aunt and uncle, Bernard and Marion Hambleton, who showed me how to combine innovation and ingenuity with the best physicians to create and operate a state-of-the-art psychiatric hospital including specialized service for people with any type of memory-impairing disease.

To my co-founder and friend, Steve Winner, whose expertise and passion for creating quality of life for people with memory-impairing diseases of all types is truly exceptional.

To my children, Heather, Aaron, Christine, John-Colby and Arianna, each of whom is a part of my reason for being.

To my loving wife, Suzanne, who is always there for me – my greatest cheerleader, confidante and best friend.

From Steve

To Dr. Wolf Wolfensberger, who showed me the intrinsic values in everyone.

To Kennon S. Shea, who gave me the freedom and encouragement to be creative.

To Richard Mendlen, who taught me how to lead others with love and strength.

To Jack Peters, who has supported Silverado and me every day with his knowledge, experience, keen insight and sense of humor.

To Loren Shook, my friend, mentor and inspirational leader, who found me in a niche and opened up the world.

To my daughter, Elizabeth, who filled a void in my life so deep I didn't know it was there.

To my wife, Deanelle, who stood with me through good times and bad and who fearlessly stood beside me as we rolled the dice to follow my dreams.

From Loren and Steve

To the memory of our co-founder, Jim Smith, whose courageous investment of time, money and expertise together with his extraordinary sense of humor were invaluable in creating Silverado as it is today.

We could not have built the company without the effort and support of Jim and his wife, Nancy.

TABLE OF CONTENTS

FOREWARD

New Possibilities in Memory Care: The Silverado Story is a wonderful epic of the journey of two men to make a difference in the lives of older individuals with memory-impairment. Loren Shook and Stephen Winner resolved to build care communities that would preserve the human spirit and dignity of the community residents. The dream took shape in the form of Silverado with an insistence on compassionate, excellent care that Silverado provides. Whether in a living community, at home, or in hospice, Silverado strives to make the human journey to the end of life a dignified and fulfilling one. In the book, you will find descriptions of care in the Silverado model that has transformed the lives of the memory impaired individual and in some cases has profoundly transformed the professional caregiver.

New Possibilities in Memory Care isn't just about older, memory-impaired adults. It is also about children and pets and how normalizing the lives of older individuals with memory challenges can restore them to fuller, more fruitful, and more satisfying lives. Throughout this story, the principle of commitment to normalization and allowing individuals with memory-impairment to be themselves and to participate most fully in all that life has to offer comes through loud and clear. It was this principle of normalization that brought the two men driving the Silverado philosophy together.

The book is also about patients with psychiatric conditions and individuals who are developmentally disabled. These were the backgrounds of Loren Shook and Stephen Winner respectively. They brought the lessons learned from the challenges of providing care to these individuals to bear on the care of memory impaired, older adults.

Loren Shook and Stephen Winner both have an entrepreneurial spirit. They are entrepreneurial in leading the business of memory care, franchising their philosophy and their communities, and expanding the availability of quality care to more older individuals. They have spirit in their commitment to the principle that love is stronger than fear and that loving residents can transform the lives of both the memory impaired individual and the person providing services to them.

New Possibilities in Memory Care: The Silverado Story is entertaining, it's heartwarming, and it's also a guidebook to providing better care and leading better lives.

As a scientist deeply engaged in developing new therapies for patients with Alzheimer's disease and other brain disorders, I know that the need for quality care of memory impaired adults will always be with us. The success in developing new therapies will not eliminate the need for excellent care and dignified means of traveling with people through the end of life. The Silverado Story shows how this can be achieved.

Jeffrey L. Cummings, M.D., Sc.D.
Camille and Larry Ruvo Chair for Brain Health
Director, Cleveland Clinic Lou Ruvo Center for Brain Health
Director, Center for Neurodegeneration
and Translational Neuroscience
Professor, Cleveland Clinic Lerner College of Medicine

INTRODUCTION

A renowned physician reading our story found it compelling, but he was skeptical. Could the meaningful life described in the book for people with dementia really exist? He decided to see Silverado for himself and so, unbeknown to us, he visited one of our memory care communities. He came away inspired. It was exactly as the book portrayed.

Our goal in writing New Possibilities in Memory Care: The Silverado Story was to engage more people in our mission of changing the way those with dementia are perceived, cared for and supported. We have heard from families that it has given them a new understanding of memory-impairment and unexpected hope. It has shown them the quality of care they have the right to expect and that possibilities still exist for those with dementia.

The book has become part of the curriculum for the nationally known Management of Aging Services program at the Erickson School at University of Maryland, Baltimore County. Other senior living organizations have mandated that their executives read our story so they can incorporate our practices into their programs, something we are humbled to learn is happening. The book has also drawn investors who, upon reading it, have allocated funding so that Silverado can serve people in more areas of the country.

We are especially proud to have testified on Capitol Hill before the U.S. Senate Special Committee on Aging at a forum, "Quality of Care for Alzheimer's Patients," that examined how the nation can best help those with Alzheimer's and their families have a better quality of care until a cure is found. Silverado has served as preferred memory care provider since 2008 for the NFL Player Care Foundation. The book has also captured two literary awards.

In the years since that first book was published, much has happened at Silverado. We now operate memory care communities in more states, and our Silverado At Home Care and Silverado Hospice service lines have grown considerably.

In tandem with the newest dementia research, we have formalized the "neighborhood" approach at our communities, in which residents live alongside others whose abilities match their own. Our reputation as the place that succeeds with memory-impaired people with symptoms too challenging for other organizations continues to grow. And with increasing diagnosis of early-onset dementia among those under 65, we have implemented ways to further serve these younger people.

When we founded Silverado in October 1996, we sought to create a place where the memory impaired would participate in a community with purpose and passion. It was a bold endeavor for a company that opened in just one location in June 1997, with practices that then drew skeptical looks from many experts. Through the belief and commitment of staff, families, and most of all the residents, Silverado flourished. Every day, the people in our care inspire us and provide a splendid truth: When love guides us and we refuse to succumb to fear, extraordinary things can happen.

Since the first edition of this book was published, we have received many requests for more stories about our people and our practices, leading us to write this new book. Everything you will read is true, although most names and some details have been altered to protect privacy. Here we recount the experiences of many people, over a long period of time, who believe they can change the world for the better.

Loren Shook and Stephen Winner

Chapter One

Nexus at Silverado

*Life is like riding a bicycle. To keep your
balance, you must keep moving.*

– Albert Einstein

Today we know more about what's possible in memory care than ever before. While a cure for Alzheimer's and other dementias remains elusive, there are now steps we can take to slow the progression of dementia and even delay its onset.

Back in 1996 when Silverado was founded, Steve Winner, Jim Smith and I (Loren Shook) knew through years of industry experience that it was possible to significantly improve the quality of life for people suffering from dementia. At that time, we did not know if we could slow the progression of dementia, our focus was on helping the resident and family have a better life – even with devastating diseases like Alzheimer's and Parkinson's. We were committed to the notion that with the right support, enjoyment of life did not need to end with a diagnosis. Steve, with our Silverado team, successfully combined a series of cutting-edge concepts that included a whole new model of care for the memory impaired. Our approach included giving people a purpose to live again, a chance to be needed, and the freedom to enjoy life. The new model included access to the outdoors and an environment where they could interact with pets and children daily. In short, we gave people a reason to get up in the morning!

We also made a commitment to the highest staffing ratio in the industry, providing professionally trained caregivers instructed not to restrain any resident. Our groundbreaking approach pushed many professionals and family members outside their comfort zone. Steve was on the front line to address these concerns and give people the confidence that this was going to work.

Shortly after we opened our first Silverado community in Escondido, California, we began to see success as our new approach to dementia care was implemented. It was a very exciting time. One of the tools we used was medication reduction. By reducing medications (which in many individual cases surpassed a dozen) and increasing participation in adult-appropriate activities, we began to see an increase in our residents' quality of life. Using all the principles noted above, there was a significant and measurable difference. We witnessed first-hand everything from positive mood and behavior changes to residents' ability to walk again on their own. The key to this approach was to treat residents with the same dignity and respect any adult would expect – a practice we call "normalization." It often lived up to its name; families saw it as a miracle, saying, "Wow, he looks as though he could fit into 'normal' society again."

The factors we always knew contributed to quality of life, we now know can actually slow the disease progression and may also result in physical changes within the brain. Since Silverado had been tracking quality of life indicators and clinical outcomes for 20 years, we were in a unique position to align our core values with a formal program to slow the onset and progression of dementia.

To be the first memory care provider to implement such a program, we needed to recruit someone whose experience was in line with our clinical/social hybrid approach to memory care, someone up-to-date with the world's top research on memory-impairing conditions. We needed to find the best.

The first time I ever heard of Kim Butrum was before Silverado was founded. Coincidentally, Kim was a speaker at the same event where I first met Steve Winner. She had been leading the Alzheimer's Disease Research Clinical Team at the University of California San Diego (UCSD) Medical Center. This was a very prestigious position – the research team at UCSD was known globally for discovering the Beta Amyloid plaque in the brain that causes Alzheimer's disease. Kim had worked in a variety of settings including as a Gerontological Nurse Practitioner in home health and hospice, director of a skilled nursing facility, founding director of a sub-acute rehabilitation unit, and the primary Nurse Practitioner at The Memory Center at the Seton Brain and Spine Neurology practice in Austin, Texas.

Her knowledge and passion has made her one of our country's leading experts on dementia care, and so we were honored when she joined Silverado in 2014. Her very first initiative was to take the collective knowledge of our Silverado team and top researchers, and create a program specifically to help residents in the early stages of dementia build and maintain cognitive ability.

She says, "Society's mindset has continually shifted over the past several decades. It used to be that a grandparent might develop a chronic disease, like heart disease, and we would say, 'well, there's nothing we can do about it.' Today, we know there are a lot of things we can do to prevent heart disease. Not only do we feel empowered, but we are empowered. That same mindset is how our children will view dementia – as something they have control over. At Silverado, we're at the forefront of this paradigm shift."

Inevitably, we were frustrated that there was an acceptance of what was thought to be the "normal progression" of a dementia such as Alzheimer's disease, and we disagreed with that progression; it was based on past practices in which individuals with dementia were treated as "needy" rather than as normal adults. This was no one's fault. It was simply accepted that there was no other way to provide care, and that there was no hope. We had frequently discussed this problem among our leaders, and when Kim came to Silverado she joined the conversation.

By 2014, we had statistical results showing that since 1997 our teams had succeeded in the re-ambulation of thousands of people. Further, we could point to thousands in the late stages of the disease who had regained their ability to feed themselves. We had evidenced-based clinical outcomes showing the lowest use of hospitalization and emergency room visits. And we could demonstrate significant reductions in the use of psychotropic medications for controlling behavior.

Of course, this expertise led our communities to attract residents in mid to late stages of dementia. But we were dismayed that families would seek a less expensive setting for a loved one with early-stage dementia, thinking it would be adequate until the disease progressed further. They thought they could always move to Silverado later. In a sense, we were victims of our own success! We needed to communicate to families and to some professionals that a purposeful, engagement-rich environment – supported by our well-trained team – could actually slow the progression of the disease and in the meanwhile enhance people's cognitive level. But before we could communicate this message effectively, we first wanted to be sure we were using the best techniques available.

Shortly after Kim joined us, we assigned her to study the best of the best in the country regarding their ability to improve the cognitive level of patients with dementia. She also did a careful evaluation of our services to determine what we were doing well and how we could improve. We specifically did not consider costs in this analysis, which is exactly how Steve, Jim, and I developed the first model for Silverado in 1996.

Kim started with a literature search and traveled to the best diagnostic centers, such as the Mayo Clinic and Cleveland Clinic. She scoured the country for the brilliant clinicians to see who was getting something right that we could use to better serve our residents. During the process, we all practiced Silverado's *Love is greater than fear* core operating philosophy. Out of love, we were committed to having the courage to listen with an open mind, and to change even if it proved more costly as we pursued our aspiration to be the best in the world.

Eight months later, Kim was excited to share that much of our programming was supported by top research. She suggested adding two components: The first was group therapy support for our residents. (Yes, although unheard of at the time, we would be providing a type of group therapy for people with dementia!) Kim's second suggestion was digital programming, which we had tried when it first came out, but did not find useful at the time – it was too boring for our residents. However, in subsequent years, there had been many advances in the field as well as studies to support potential benefits.

Taking Kim's findings, we resolved to overhaul our program focus and to rollout our new initiative in all Silverado memory care communities. This was a major undertaking.

In January 2015, after much anticipation, Silverado launched "Nexus". This 20-hour-a-week program is built around six brain-building "pillars" that not only make a difference in the lives of those we serve, but also help reshape the way people with dementia are perceived. We named the program Nexus (the Latin word for "connection,") because it's designed to create connections in the brain by combining science and social engagement. Silverado's six pillars of Nexus include:

(1) **Physical Exercise:** Multiple studies show a correlation between physical activity and improved brain function, which may help to slow the effects of dementia. Nexus incorporates physical exercises such as Ping-Pong, strength training, aerobics, golf and other activities.

(2) **Stress Reduction:** Studies reveal that meditation and other stress-relieving activities benefit people with Mild Cognitive Impairment (MCI). Nexus includes mindfulness-based activity such as meditation, Tai Chi and yoga.

(3) **Cognitive Exercise:** Cognitive compensation strategies reinforce

cognitive strengths for those with early-stage dementia. Journaling, word strategy games, and creative arts are some of the ways these individuals may be able to slow their disease progression.

(4) Specialized Digital Programs: Nexus uses digital tablets equipped with a specially designed brain fitness program called Brain HQ by Posit Science. Based on the science and research of neuroplasticity, targeted brain exercises have been shown to reinvigorate certain brain functions. Outcomes include improved visual and auditory processing speed, sharper attention, and better memory.

(5) Purposeful Social Activities: Purposeful social activities and a strong social network may protect against cognitive decline and modify the effect of Alzheimer's disease. As part of Nexus, purposeful social activities include teaching skills to others, and participation in service clubs that benefit the greater community.

(6) Resident Support Groups: While traditional support groups have been for caregivers, studies now show that support groups can benefit people with dementia by reducing depression and improving self-esteem. One of our social workers, Melissa Cruz, LMSW, presented her research on this powerful component of the Nexus program at the Alzheimer's Association International Conference in 2015.

> "If Nexus were a drug, it would be a multi-billion dollar drug."
> -Loren Shook

In the first year we implemented Nexus, early results surpassed our greatest expectations. Hundreds of Silverado residents began benefiting immediately. We track the effect of Nexus using a variety of tools, but we primarily use the Mini Mental State Examination (MMSE). This 11-question exam is recognized industry-wide as a method of monitoring progression in Alzheimer's disease. Neurologists, social workers, and gerontologists often use this test. It has a scoring scale of zero (severe dementia) to 30 (no dementia), to monitor disease progression over time. To get a baseline score, every Silverado resident takes the MMSE within two weeks of arrival. Every six months afterward, we retest residents as part of their personalized care plan. After just six months, we began to see the MMSE scores of some of our Nexus residents improve significantly. And although only time will give us more scientific results, we are seeing this improvement throughout our communities – a testament to the skill and knowledge of our team.

"In addition to the core research and new findings, a number of individuals inspired us as we developed Nexus," expresses Kim. "One was a friend from the University of California Irvine who had led studies and presented findings regarding the impact that exercise has on the brain. I had heard him speak a decade earlier, and he was never one to overstate his results. So when he said, 'We now have enough evidence to say with certainly that exercise is a lifestyle factor that helps to maintain a healthy brain,' I was ecstatic. This was one of the studies that truly changed our thinking as we focused on implementing a brain health component to our program."

"We like to say that the side effect of Nexus is quality of life."
-Loren Shook

If Nexus were a drug, it would be a multi-billion dollar drug. Medications currently available to treat Alzheimer's have shown only moderate improvements of 1-2 points on the MMSE, benefits which last about half a year in most people. Neurologists expect an average decline on the MMSE of 2-4 points a year in Alzheimer's. With Nexus implemented in the Silverado environment, we quickly began to see some MMSE scores improve by three, four, and even five points. To see stabilization or improvement in cognitive scores is exciting. While research is still ongoing, it is clear Silverado's six pillars of brain health can alter the trajectory of dementia for many people.

This. Is. Groundbreaking. Nexus programming, within Silverado's clinical/social care environment, helps hundreds of people with dementia each year to delay the issues of mobility, health, and behavioral issues. Not many years ago, researchers could only dream of results like this. What we're doing today significantly changes the quality of life for residents now, and it sets the stage for years to come.

Life is about living. A dementia diagnosis does not mean the end of a purposeful life. Nexus is enabling people with memory loss to live a better quality of life every single day.

"The Nexus program guides people in a step-by-step program to brain health. Human memory and thinking are complex and the Nexus program addresses this complexity through brain and body programs that provide the building blocks of brain health and brain function."

- Jeffrey L. Cummings, M.D., Sc.D.

"Another inspiration for Nexus was the 'nun study,' chronicled in a book called *Aging with Grace*," shares Kim. "In 1986, 678 Catholic Sisters began participating in a brain study that concluded in 2001. Using information dating back to when each participant first became a nun and combining it with 15 years of tests and observations, Dr. David Snowdon, a leading expert on Alzheimer's disease, discovered a striking positive impact that living a purposeful life can have on the brain: While some of the participant's brain pathology indicated they had dementia, they displayed no noticeable signs of cognitive impairment during life. It was a remarkable study, and inspired the Purposeful Social Activity pillar of Nexus."

The vision we established at our founding back in 1996 continues to guide us today. We aim to change the way the world cares for and perceives people with cognitive decline. True to Silverado's culture, we regularly share details of our Nexus program with others, here in the United States and abroad. In April 2016, Kim Butrum, along with Nexus co-creator, Kathy Greene, presented the Nexus program and its early results to attendees of the Alzheimer's Disease International conference in Budapest, Hungary. The topic of the 31st annual event was Dementia: Global Perspective – Local Solutions. Alongside others who influence global progress in treating and preventing Alzheimer's, the duo presented evidence that current research can be successfully implemented daily within a memory care setting. To the global leaders in attendance, their presentation was of scientific interest, but for people with memory loss the result was life-giving.

Six months after implementing Nexus, we also broadened the definition of a Nexus resident. The maximum MMSE score is 30 points – no dementia. A score of 20 to 24 suggests mild dementia, 13 to 20 suggests moderate dementia, and less than 12 indicates severe dementia. When we first set out, we enrolled anyone with a 20 or higher on the MMSE (mild dementia). After witnessing dramatic results, we altered the parameter to 15 or higher. It quickly became apparent that people in the mid-stage of the disease process could also benefit greatly. (Of course, even individuals in the later stages continued to take part in Silverado's sensory programs).

When it was clear that Nexus was a powerful force for change, we expanded the program to maximize quality of life for individuals with mild cognitive impairment who live outside the Silverado community. The robust brain fitness program first became available in Los Angeles, California in 2015. Participants, who live at home or at an independent living community, regularly visit the Silverado community where they are given access to a variety of support groups, social outings, brain fitness workshops, and other resources.

"Recently, I transferred a few residents from another dementia directed care facility to Silverado. I had them enrolled into the Nexus program and the results were amazing. They went from an apathetic/depressed mood to being happy and heavily engaged in activities. What a great program for improving the quality of life for patients with dementia."

- Walter J. Nieri, M.D., AGSF, FACP, CMD

Because Nexus quickly became a way of life, we realized that it could be taught and implemented in a variety of settings. In 2015, it was estimated that more than 800,000 people were living alone at home with dementia, and that number sadly continues to grow. Knowing this, we began in 2016 to look at ways to bring Nexus into people's homes. The truth is, dementia has a large and growing effect on the healthcare system as a whole. The rules of healthcare are changing. New, progressive hospital systems are constantly challenging various healthcare providers to work together and think outside the box to give patients the right level of care. Hospital leaders have identified both the challenge of caring for dementia patients and the burden it places on their nursing staff. Healthcare systems are more and more trusting Silverado with direct hospital discharges to our memory care communities. Families want to know that their loved one with dementia is transitioning to the place best equipped to handle unique needs – whether at home, a skilled nursing facility, an assisted living facility, or a memory care community. Anyone would want access to a program like Nexus for a loved one. Unfortunately, dementia patients spend too many days either in the hospital or discharged to a setting not appropriate for their condition. Too often this results in additional medications to manage behaviors, which in turn, leads to reduced mobilization, increased risk of developing pressure ulcers, and weight loss – all while increasing costs to the healthcare system. When we look at the state of healthcare today, we want to be a solution. Hospitals and other healthcare systems are quickly realizing that sending their patients to a Silverado community, or home with the "Nexus At Home" program, reduces the likelihood that they will return to the hospital. Nexus changes individual lives, and it also has the power to better serve society as a whole as the delivery of healthcare continues to transform.

At its core, Nexus at Silverado is about the former piano teacher who begins making music again, the cartoonist who once again makes his friends laugh, the poet who writes new poetry despite his dementia, and the artist who hosts an art exhibit–things no one ever dreamed could be a reality for someone with dementia. We've encountered these types of successes over the past 20 years, but today Nexus gives us an opportunity to facilitate an increase in the number of these stories. After all, this is what continues to inspire us to be the best in the world.

In Budapest, Kathy Greene, who serves as our Senior Vice President of Programs and Services Integration, expressed to the audience, "The bottom line is that the outcomes are spectacular. No one in assisted living gets outcomes like these, and we are excited to share this knowledge to make a positive impact on more people around the globe. At Silverado, we regularly refine our programs based on two things: observations made within our communities and the latest research studies. Nexus is just the beginning. We will continue to gain new knowledge and implement new programs with one purpose: to improve the lives of those affected by Alzheimer's disease and other memory impairing conditions."

Kathy's right. We're not resting on our laurels. I'm often asked why others in the industry don't have the same program. The short answer: It's not easy to bring a program like Nexus to life. It takes individualized focus and an industry-leading team with proven outcomes to make it a reality. At Silverado, we are humbled to be in a position to create innovative programs like Nexus. To better understand how we got here, it's important to learn about our past and what drives us. That said, here's our story.

Chapter Two

Love is Greater than Fear

May I have the courage today, To live the life that I would love,
To postpone my dream no longer, But do at last what I came here for,
And waste my heart on fear no more.

– John O'Donoghue

At one of the lowest points of his life, Loren Shook went to a retreat high in the California mountains. Two days later, he was a man committed to change.

Loren was already a successful entrepreneur. He had built a flourishing business dedicated to giving meaning to the lives of people with Alzheimer's and other memory-impairing diseases.

However, he was living with a sense of failure. Despite his professional success, his marriage was ending. And he had an uneasiness and dissatisfaction about decisions he was making. His long-time friend and executive coach, Vance Caesar, was about to change that.

Every year, Vance invited Loren to take part in a weekend men's retreat in the San Jacinto Mountains. After years of politely declining, Loren surprised himself by accepting the offer.

That Saturday, he and a dozen other business leaders arrived at a lodge perched between two expanses of towering rock. The setting seemed to be nature's way of encouraging introspection. When Vance beckoned the men into a circle in the living room and began talking about happiness,

Loren was ready to listen to Vance explain that throughout the centuries, great philosophers and religious leaders have concluded there are two core emotions from which all other feelings spring – Love and Fear. He elaborated, "Those who achieve the most happiness have based their decisions and actions on love, not fear. They have acted in the best interest of the people around them rather than in fear, anger, and defensiveness – negative emotions which arise when we feel threatened or unsure of ourselves."

Looking intently at each man, he added, "Most of us grew up with fear. It wasn't the A on the report card that got our parents' attention; it was the C. In a sense, it was their fear speaking – if you failed, it meant they had failed.

"As adults," Vance continued, "we perpetuate our childhood experiences. Looking around the room, I see overachievers who have allowed fear to shape countless decisions leading to current circumstances."

Vance let that sink in and then approached an issue that is difficult for men. "Might you accomplish more by accepting love as your navigator? If you will choose to live your life based on love, you will find people are drawn to you. You will develop better relationships. You will be happier in your personal life. This is the challenge: Stop living a life shaped by fear. Dare to change and let love be your guide."

The words hit Loren like a lightning bolt. From the earliest days of his childhood, his will to succeed by doing the right thing had characterized his life. No one could argue with its effectiveness. It had brought him undeniable success.

But at that moment at the lodge, Loren realized there is only one way to truly know what the right thing is – by making choices and acting on the greatest positive emotion: Love.

As he reflected on Vance's words, he knew it was too late to cope with his failed marriage, and he didn't know if he could treat every single future decision with love. But he wanted to try it. A phrase flashed in his mind, which would become his polestar.

Love is greater than fear.

On the drive down the mountain, Loren resolved to tell Silverado's executive team about the concept.

But when the company vice presidents gathered at the monthly meeting in the corporate conference room, the normally punctual Loren retreated twice to his desk before summoning the courage to leave his office.

"They're going to think I'm nuts," he thought. "Guys don't talk about love." Then, bracing himself, he countered, "Loren, you're a chicken, a gutless wonder, reacting from fear. You need to come from love. So you're going to bring it up." And he did.

Surprised silence and impassive expressions greeted Loren's talk about love being greater than fear. A few faces turned ashen and others smiled cautiously when he finished by proposing that Silverado adopt the concept as its core operating principle. With Loren's prodding, discussion ensued and, eventually, the executives reached a consensus: The idea was good, but it would be better if "love" weren't involved. Perhaps "like" or "strongly like" might take its place.

"But this is exactly the point," Loren said. "We're all afraid of the word 'love.' Think about it: we want the staff to do 'the right thing' with our residents. But it's just a hollow phrase if they don't have the criteria for determining it. As the company expands, it will be hard for newer employees to understand and carry out our vision. But if we tell our employees to serve residents from the standpoint of love, they will naturally fulfill our expectations."

Steve was intrigued by the concept and the teachings behind it. After the meeting, he went to the library to find out more and came home with an armload of books. He quickly saw how beneficial it would be for the company.

Loren set about introducing *Love is greater than fear* throughout Silverado.

He brought the same fire to this endeavor that he had brought to building the company from scratch. He dedicated time to group training and one-on-one conversations with staff.

At first, some in management resisted the philosophy, fearing to give up control with the new approach. Loren recalls, they would ask, "Why risk it when everything is going so well?"

On the other hand, the caregivers, housekeepers, culinary staff, maintenance people, and others who work most directly with residents responded without hesitation. "Of course we will act through love. That's why we're here."

Employees began saying that *Love is greater than fear* was changing their lives at home as well as in the workplace. It was helping them to communicate with spouses and children and to mend relationships damaged by anger and regret.

Loren knew this principle had the power to improve life for everyone, regardless of financial status or personal circumstances. Years later, he remains awed by its powerful reach. He is convinced that *Love is greater than fear* can yield remarkable transformations on a wide scale.

As evidence of this, professional associations and boards of directors at other companies frequently invite him to speak. As he discusses Silverado and its vision of creating a better life for the memory impaired, he asserts, "It's impossible to understand Silverado without knowing its guiding principle." When someone responds, "I would love to do this at my business, but I wouldn't dare," it fills him with regret, because he knows they are motivated by fear.

People who have known Loren a long time can see that *Love is greater than fear* has wrought a major change in him. Loren's moral compass had never been in doubt, but he began to measure his words more carefully, and many times to soften his tone. He was quicker to trust and forgive. Even his body seemed looser, in greater sync with his emotional and physical surroundings.

"Think of it as a scale," he suggests, "with fear at zero and love at 100. If you can make love-based choices 85 to 90 percent of the time, then for you, *Love is greater than fear*. This is what we believe, what we live by at Silverado. It's what I've committed my life to."

Chapter Three

The Need to Be Understood

Whether we name divine presence synchronicity, serendipity, or graced moment matters little. What matters is the reality that our hearts have been understood. Nothing is as real as a healthy dose of magic, which restores our spirits.

– Nancy Long

The glossy palomino accompanied Loren across the leafy grounds, horse and teenager matching paces. As they neared the hospital, a nurse rolled Janet's wheelchair out the door and onto the wide driveway. It wasn't the first time Loren had noticed this patient. Appearing to be in her late twenties, she might have been pretty if her features had displayed any animation, but with her head tilted down and her eyes unfocused, her face was a mask of stillness. Her body was motionless and rigid.

Janet hadn't made a sound since she arrived at Fairfax Hospital the previous week. She didn't flinch when a nurse inserted a needle into her arm to give her fluids. When a doctor entered her room and asked her questions, she remained impassive. Holding her right wrist, he raised her arm above her head. When he let go, it stayed in this awkward position, as if she were a department store mannequin.

Catatonia is not necessarily a diagnosis but rather a descriptive term for a presentation of a variety of symptoms.

After a few moments, the doctor gently lowered her arm. Janet had a classic case of catatonia, the unresponsive state first described in 1874 by German psychiatrist Karl Ludwig Kahlbaum.

On this day in the early 1970s, scientists had not yet developed the drugs that would become standard treatment for mental disorders. As such, Fairfax Hospital treated catatonia, depression, schizophrenia, dementia, and other maladies of the mind by examining their patients' life stories. They explored who these people were before illness gripped their psyches. They discovered what had motivated them and what had mattered to them. Then, using the collected information, they designed treatments unique to each person.

When Janet first arrived, a Fairfax social worker questioned her family closely and learned she loved horses. As a child, Janet had lived down the road from a farm. Every day after school, she went to curry a stallion and two mares and muck out their stalls. In exchange, she was allowed to ride them. When she matured into adulthood and moved away, her labor of love ended.

Loren was not surprised when the nurse told him to go to the pasture and bring a horse for Janet. Fairfax Hospital's approach to psychiatric treatment was a way of life for him. His aunt and uncle owned the 20-acre facility, and Loren's family lived in a two-room house on the hospital grounds. At 19, Loren had already been working at Fairfax for four years. He was a "gofer," mopping floors, helping patients with showers, washing dishes, raking leaves, and relieving the nursing staff during breaks. Loren was expected to do whatever needed to be done at any given moment. The hospital kept the palomino, named Heidi, and two other horses among a menagerie that included dogs, peacocks, pheasants, and chickens. The grounds included fragrant gardens, meandering paths, rolling lawns shaded by a canopy of maple and oak trees, and a stream so clear that salmon spawned there every year. The verdant setting itself was a treatment tool at Fairfax Hospital. Fresh air, nature's rhythms, and the company of animals often reconnected patients to the world.

Each time Loren approached the pasture, Heidi would come to the fence to nuzzle him. The palomino was a "people horse," stepping forward for caresses and carrots while her pasture-mates retreated.

Now, with Loren at her side, Heidi clopped onto the pavement and halted in front of Janet. The sun was bright, but Janet didn't blink, even as the big horse drew close.

There was a long hush in which even the birds seemed to hold their breath.

Suddenly, Janet stretched out her arm – the same one the doctor had raised and lowered. She touched Heidi with a finger. Then, she laid her whole hand on the palomino's warm side and began to stroke her. After a few moments, she pushed herself up and out of the wheelchair. She grasped Heidi's face and leaned in close to speak to her.

Her tone was urgent, yet soft. Loren and the others couldn't make out what she was saying. They didn't try. This was a private communication of souls between a long-mute woman and an empathic horse. Three weeks later, Janet walked out of Fairfax Hospital and went home, her spirit and life restored. Loren never saw her again. But the conversation he couldn't hear on the driveway that day would somehow echo decades later.

A dog does a quick barking dance for a biscuit dangling just out of reach.

Rubber soles squeak as a grinning toddler makes a dash across shiny tiles.

Chairs scrape up to a table and hammers begin pounding nails into wood.

A male voice calls out: "We need you at men's club," and another answers: "I'm coming, I'm coming."

Out of sight, drums thump in varying tones and rhythms.

The front door swings open with a whoosh. Three teenagers spill in, all talking at once.

Silverado is a noisy place.

People aren't here to rest or slip quietly from society. They come here to live. They are people with Alzheimer's disease, vascular dementia, Parkinson's, and a host of other memory-impairing illnesses.

As these conditions progress, speech and reason deteriorate. The easy familiarity of the loving spouse of fifty years, the dependable parent, or the sibling with tandem experiences seems to be over.

Until you step into Silverado.

At Silverado's core, there's a knowledge that can transform the lives of the memory-impaired, while enriching the souls of everyone around them. This knowledge puts aside fear and replaces it with love.

The staff at Silverado knows that the human spirit glows until we take our last breath. While memory-impairment erodes the spirit's ability to express itself through what is considered normal words and actions, it doesn't mean the spirit is not present; it still shines, but "speaks" differently. By devoting time, effort, and love to accepting the memory-impaired as they are and by discovering new ways to communicate, we can build new relationships with them. It's like learning a new language.

This is the vision of Silverado.

We all have a need to love and be loved; a need to be understood and appreciated, to surge through the day with purpose. A need to enjoy simple pleasures: to bask in the warmth of sunshine and to connect with animals, children, and flowers. These needs never change, regardless of the effects of memory disorders.

> Alzheimer's disease is a progressive disease that attacks the brain and results in impaired memory, thinking and behavior.

For those of us with unimpaired memory, life is linear. We mature from children to teenagers to adults. Last year, this year. Yesterday, today, tomorrow. But for people with memory-impairment, today could be twenty years ago. An adult child can be mistaken for a long-deceased mother.

When those we love start stepping off the straight chronological line, we try desperately to refocus them. No, today is Tuesday. I'm not your mother; I'm your daughter. Don't you remember we already ate lunch?

When we realize we can't fix their memories, many of us withdraw. What's the point of trying to connect when they won't remember? Why not just keep these frail, confused people safe, comfortable, clean, and fed?

Because there is a better way.

Silverado is a memory care organization whose vision isn't really about memory. The memory-impaired don't need linear thoughts and words to connect when joy, touch, hugs, smiles, and laughter are the language. It's about reaching and nurturing the human spirit. The day of the week doesn't matter. What matters is that the day has meaning.

How does Silverado do this?

Animals are central at Silverado – at least one dog and one cat for every twenty-five residents; one bird or more for every four people who reside at a Silverado community; a burbling tank with colorful fish for every forty.

Who would expect that minimum numbers of resident animals would be a fundamental rule in memory care? But Silverado's forty-page copyrighted pet care manual spells out the regulations clearly. That barking dog leaping for a treat is one of more than 600 non-humans – including rabbits, guinea pigs and even miniature horses, – living permanently in Silverado communities. They're joined by pets that move in with residents and by others who accompany staff to work each day.

For those with memory impairment the idea of participating in a "club" is more familiar than a group. This concept promotes membership, holding a special position, and some exclusivity which supports self-esteem.

Children are important too – the child barreling through a living room and the teens arriving in a chatty swarm. Silverado even encourages employees to bring their own children to work with them. So you see infants slumbering in residents' laps and toddlers taking their first steps in Silverado's hallways. School buses chug up in front of Silverado's communities and drop off youngsters who burst through the doors to spend the afternoon participating in activities alongside residents, helping care for the pets, or sitting quietly to study.

The frontotemporal dementias (FTD) are a group of degenerative brain disorders that share many clinical features.

Purpose feeds the spirit, as well. A man who has always loved woodworking may have lost the ability to express his interest in ways we recognize, but he hasn't lost his passion for meaningful activity. At Silverado, he won't craft his wood projects alone. Other residents and staff will work next to him, because a passion shared with friends is more satisfying. This understanding underlies our "club concept." In the drum circle, for instance, residents come together to thump out rhythmic expressions that humans have enjoyed for ages.

The relief, the pleasure, the dignity of normal: this is part of life at Silverado where activities reflect the interests of adults. Silverado residents garden, cook, create music, and paint. They consider current events. They do not toss balloons, swaddle dolls, or stare at cartoons – unless they have always enjoyed cartoons. The changes wrought by memory disorder may seem to turn grown-ups into children, but the practice of giving them childish games and toys dulls the spirit. It's also the first step toward isolating them in a less-than-normal social space. As a society, we often treat people with memory disorders as though they have something the rest of us might catch. When they become less able to participate in normal life and their behavior strays from the linear path, we quarantine them behind drawn shades and closed doors at home or in institutions, where few but staff and dutiful family ever appear.

Their memory-impairment frightens us, confuses us, angers us. Sometimes, what they do and say repulses us. The common courtesy of being looked in the eye when addressed can quickly erode. But when we stop nurturing their spirit through meaningful connection with the world, we hasten their decline. Depression, loneliness, and feelings of worthlessness aggravate their symptoms and their overall health.

Hoping to galvanize America's attention, experts in public policy and health call the rise in memory-impairing diseases an epidemic. Doctors diagnose a new case of Alzheimer's every 66 seconds. According to the Alzheimer's Association, 5.4 million Americans have the disease. And nearly 15 million Americans provide unpaid care for people with Alzheimer's and other dementias. Within forty years, as many as 16 million more Americans could develop memory impairment. The worldwide figure may exceed 131 million.

America's propensity to solve all ailments with pills contributes to the sad lives that so many of the memory-impaired endure. Loading more prescriptions into their bodies to "get their behavior under control" is the easiest solution in today's world. So they swallow as many as fifteen different drugs a day. Those who don't sink into a near constant sleep often lash out verbally and physically. What's mistaken for incurable aggression in the memory-impaired is the spirit's cry of protest against the regimen that suffocates their self-expression.

Current research is primarily seeking a pharmacological cure for memory impairment as well as a way to prevent it in the first place. This quest dominates media coverage of Alzheimer's and shapes the public discussion. While strongly supporting this research, Silverado also passionately leads the way to improve the daily lives of those with memory impairment in the here and now.

What if as a society we overcame our fear of Alzheimer's disease and responded to it with love? What if this disease represented an opportunity? What if we accepted and embraced those with memory impairment? We would discover what Silverado experiences every day: our own spirit flourishes through selfless love and service to the memory impaired.

Tom arrived in a wheelchair, head and body leaning to one side, his skin like yellowing tissue paper loosely draped over bones. As Sheila, a Silverado caregiver, rolled him through wide bright hallways, she spoke gently in welcome, explaining where he was going and what he could expect. But only his wife, Dorothy, walking beside him, responded. Tom had not spoken in a long time. Nor had he eaten or taken any notice of the world through eyes that seemed permanently shut.

Tom had been in a hospital for weeks. Physicians couldn't pinpoint the cause of his nearly vegetative state. He was in his eighties, and other medical issues complicated his Alzheimer's disease. The doctors had told Dorothy that Tom had just a week or two to live. So, on this morning, an ambulance delivered Tom to Silverado to spend his last days.

A large window brought sunshine and the vista of a blooming backyard into the room chosen for him. Sheila didn't know whether Tom would ever open his eyes again, but ever the optimist, she positioned his bed so he had a view of the outdoors. Once she got Tom settled, she and Dorothy turned toward the dresser to unpack his suitcase.

The two women talked quietly, Dorothy occasionally falling silent as she folded the clothing that was as much a part of her life as her husband's. The red flannel shirt, Tom's uniform on weekend mornings, and the beige cardigan he wore while reading on the patio.

Suddenly, the sheets rustled. The bed shifted with a small thud.

"Was that a horse I just saw?"

Sheila and Dorothy turned. Tom was sitting up, stretching forward toward the window, eyes wide in a blue gleam. Sheila went to the window to open it and leaned out. Two miniature horses, one silvery and the other black with gray flecks, were sauntering along further down the yard. Sheila looked back at Tom. Dorothy was clasping his hand to her cheek as she stooped down to his face.

"I never thought I would hear your voice again," she whispered to him. Looking up at Sheila with tears in her eyes, she added, "My husband has a soft spot for horses."

Tom spent much of the next afternoon in Silverado's garden. There, he relished Dorothy's company and velvety nuzzles by Hocus Pocus and Lil' Rascal, the two little horses which had passed by Tom's window. The man whom doctors predicted would soon pass noiselessly from the world confounded their expectations. Tom's memory remained impaired and his body fragile, but his spirit glowed again.

Sheila had been a caregiver at Silverado from the beginning. The sight of Tom and his wife sitting together in the sunlight, chatting and laughing, still stands out as one of her best memories. She reminisces, "Tom's family had tried everything before he came here. His wife Dorothy felt she had already lost him. She hadn't realized that his eyes were open just enough that his spirit could still watch the world. Who would have thought a pair of horses could accomplish what the doctors hadn't been able to do!"

Chapter Four

Overcoming Stigma

Never believe that a few caring people can't change the world.
For, indeed, that's all who ever have.

– Margaret Mead

Vic was driving home from his office in stop-and-go traffic, mulling over a project due at the end of the month. Suddenly, it struck him that he should drop by his church. Not having any reason to go in the middle of the week, he shrugged off the thought. But over the next few miles the idea kept returning, pressing at him. Vic decided that God must be directing him there, although he could not imagine why. He took the next exit, pulled into the church parking lot a few minutes later and headed toward the entrance. Noticing a man seated on a bench in the adjacent patio, he paused.

"Have we met before?" Vic asked. "My name's Vic."

After a moment of silence, the man stood. He had a robust build, salt-and-pepper hair, and silver-rimmed glasses. "I'm Leyland," he said, and the two shook hands.

"It sure is a beautiful evening," said Vic.

Leyland cleared his throat. "I guess so. To tell you the truth, I hadn't noticed."

He sat back down on one end of the bench, leaving plenty of room for Vic, who accepted the unspoken invitation and took a seat.

"Have you been with this church long?" Vic asked.

"A few years."

"I've been coming for quite a while myself," said Vic. "It's an important part of my life." When Leyland made no comment, Vic risked another question. "What brings you here this evening?"

Leyland knotted his hands, looked down at his lap, and drew in a breath. "I think I have Alzheimer's disease." Exhaling with a ragged noise, he crossed his arms over his stomach and doubled over. "I was at home thinking of a way to kill myself, and I decided to come here first. I don't know why."

His face creasing with concern, Vic put his hand on Leyland's arm. "I am so glad I stopped to talk to you. Please believe me that life is still worth living. This isn't the end. I know because my mother has Alzheimer's."

Alice had begun calling Vic several times a day, asking him the same questions over and over. At first, Vic attributed his mother's forgetfulness to the pressure of caring for her husband during his battle with leukemia. Later, he attributed it to her grief at his death. She had been married to Vic's father, Big John, a renowned drag racer, for nearly sixty years. Their lives were intertwined not only by their love and the two children they raised, but also by Alice's dedication to the behind-the-scenes aspect of her husband's career.

The reality that his mother had dementia became clear the day Vic's niece phoned him at work. She told him that Alice had run out of the house and fled into the middle of the street screaming for the police. His niece followed her to get her to come back inside, but Alice swung her purse at the girl and shouted to leave her alone. Vic dashed out of his office to his car and headed for his mother's house. On the way, he called her doctor to describe the situation and ask what he should do.

"She has anti-anxiety medication," the physician said. "Tell her to take it."

"But we aren't going to be able to get close enough to her to get her to do that," Vic said.

"Then crush the pills, put them in some pudding and offer it to her," the doctor responded curtly.

"You don't understand," Vic said, raising his voice. "She's taking a swing at anyone who approaches her. She's not about to stand there eating pudding."

"Well, the only other option is calling 911," the physician said. "The fire department will come out and put her in restraints. Then she can have an injection to calm her down."

Telling the doctor he was not going to subject his mother to a straitjacket, Vic ended the conversation. As he neared Alice's house, he began praying for the strength and skills to cope with what he was about to encounter. When he arrived, he found his niece and several other family members standing in a circle around Alice, out of arm's reach. Taking a deep breath, Vic approached the group.

Alice looked at him. In a calm voice, she asked," What are you doing here?"

"I came to talk to you," Vic said, his tone matching hers. "Let's go inside and sit down." She nodded and followed him into the house.

That was when Vic began caring for his mother in his own home. His experience inspired him to help others whose loved ones had dementia. As he led Alzheimer's support groups at his church, he began to understand something he had heard his pastor say: "God never wastes a hurt." Vic found that providing emotional and spiritual support to other people brought him a sense of purpose that had been lacking in his career as a mortgage broker.

As he began to wonder whether he could make a living by helping others deal with dementia, a friend referred him to Loren Shook. What was supposed to be a thirty-minute appointment turned into a three-hour meeting. Vic spoke with passion about the need to educate churches on dementia issues. The faith-based community could take on a major role in assisting individuals and families dealing with Alzheimer's. Loren listened intently, occasionally nodding, and then spontaneously invited members of Silverado's executive team to join the conversation with Vic.

Silverado has since hired Vic as Senior Director of Faith Outreach to handle Alzheimer's education and to build relationships with churches. In affiliation with Silverado, Vic created the Mind Heart Soul Ministry at Saddleback Church not only to serve the memory-impaired, but also to provide education and support for the families and loved ones of those afflicted.

Embarking on this career brought Vic into a new phase of his life. Each day, he woke feeling he was making a difference. The next year, his mother moved to Silverado. Years later, Vic was certain she was living longer and more happily in Silverado's care than she would have if she had remained in his home.

Leyland, hearing that Vic's mother had Alzheimer's, sat back from his doubled-over position. He didn't say anything, but when he turned to look at Vic, it was with encouragement for him to continue.

"Why do you think you have Alzheimer's?" Vic asked.

"I had a big presentation to clients yesterday and when I got there, I realized I had forgotten all of my notes." He paused and said, "It's the second time I've done something like that in the past month. Then, I was sending a birthday card to my twin granddaughters and I couldn't remember their names." Raising his hands to clutch his forehead, he added, "I can't imagine telling my family. What would my friends say if they knew? I'm going to be a useless burden on other people, a crazy person. It's better for everyone if I finish it now."

"Alzheimer's doesn't have to mean any of those things, and it's not about being crazy," Vic said. "It's a disease, not a mental problem. May I ask, have you seen a doctor?"

"No," Leyland answered. "I can't bear the thought of hearing the diagnosis. If you told me I had anything else wrong with me, anything at all, I could handle it. But not this."

"Leyland, I understand how upset you are, but it's by no means certain you have Alzheimer's," Vic said. "A lot of things can cause forgetfulness. Sometimes it's from stress or, if you're taking medications, it might be a side effect. Those are just a couple of examples. Please don't assume you have Alzheimer's when you haven't talked to a physician."

Leyland didn't say anything.

"But if it turns out that you are developing Alzheimer's, it's not a reason to take your life. Think about the people who love you and how devastated they would be. I am sure you wouldn't want to hurt your family and friends that way."

"They'd be better off without me," came the quick response. "I'll be talking nonsense, not able to do anything worthwhile anymore, not even capable of going out in public."

"Leyland, every day I see people with Alzheimer's who are leading full lives. They're doing volunteer work, painting, golfing, building things, going out to eat. They make new friends; their families love spending time with them. Many of them have had Alzheimer's for years."

Leyland didn't say anything, but he turned slightly toward Vic, who took it as a positive sign.

Vic continued, "Is life the same as before they developed the disease? No, it's different, but it is still worth living. They feel that way and their families and friends feel that way, too."

Leyland reached into his pocket to pull out a handkerchief. He removed his glasses, wiped them, and put them back on. Then he said, "Please, tell me. How could that be possible?"

Vic and Leyland talked for almost an hour.

Vic said: "God has our lives planned from the time we're born. He knows everything that's going to happen to us. He never wants to hurt us. He only wants to help us become more like Christ. My mother didn't want Alzheimer's. I'm angry she has it. But because of Mom's disease, I started volunteering to help thousands of people. If you do have the disease, God has a reason. And He's the only one who knows the reason. If we're faithful and obedient, He will lead us to a fantastic future that we can't even imagine."

Leyland started crying and hugged Vic. "Thank you," Leyland said. "I never thought of it that way."

As they stood up to leave, Leyland promised he wouldn't do anything drastic and that he would call for a doctor's appointment the next morning. Vic gave him his card, asking Leyland to phone him if he ever felt despair again. Leyland agreed he would.

Vic never heard from him. But several months later in the friendly hubbub after a church service, he noticed Leyland on the other side of the large sanctuary. He was talking and laughing with a silver-haired woman, a younger couple, and two little girls.

In 2006, Lynda Hogg learned she had Alzheimer's disease. She later wrote in an essay: "In my experience, it is at the point of diagnosis or shortly afterwards that stigma begins to appear. It is as if friends and relatives can accept and be amused by someone's foibles prior to the diagnosis and can warmly comment that they are getting eccentric. However, once dementia is diagnosed, it's as if a line has been crossed, and some people don't want to be associated with an illness affecting the brain."

Her writing appeared in "Overcoming the Stigma of Dementia," the 2012 report produced by Alzheimer's Disease International, a global federation of associations dedicated to helping those with dementia. Surveying memory-impaired people and their families in fifty-four countries, the study revealed that more than two-thirds of respondents believe dementia carries a stigma.

One memory-impaired person answering the poll said "People think those with dementia are crazy, mentally unglued, and unstable and therefore, to be avoided, because how would you know how to communicate with them anyway? Many people are afraid of dementia...and want to stay as far away from it as possible. It terrifies them."

In a society that values youth, physical strength, prestigious careers, and fashionable possessions, the elderly and infirm lack status. As their conditions progress, they are stigmatized because there is less and less about them with which society can relate. Unfortunately, this stigma prevents many people from seeking early diagnosis.

Lucia Dattoma, M.D., who specializes in geriatric medicine at UCLA Health in Los Angeles, sees this reality firsthand. "I do believe Alzheimer's and other dementias have a stigma," she said. "The diagnosis can bring fear and shame. Often, one of the first reactions is 'What am I going to tell my family and friends?'"

"The stigma can even effect doctors. I've seen patients with obvious signs of memory-impairment whose regular physicians have said nothing to them about it because they aren't comfortable with it," she said. "When I bring it up with the families, they ask me, 'Why didn't the other doctor discuss it?'"

According to Joe W. Ramsdell, M.D., Professor and Division Head, General Internal Medicine at the University of California, San Diego, "When we can diagnose early, we are able to talk with patients and their families about how the memory impaired can still enjoy a good quality of life. We can explain what certain behaviors mean, and give caregivers insight regarding what to expect.

"Early diagnosis also enables us to help the patient and family build a support system. It allows those with dementia to decide how they would like to live and to receive care, so that they can be involved in determining their own future quality of life."

When memory impairment is detected early, there is also time to determine whether there could be any benefit in trying drugs to slow the progression of Alzheimer's. Experts are tempered in their views of the effectiveness of these medications. Dr. Dattoma believes they can potentially slow the disease's progress for as little as six months or as much as three years, but emphasizes that every person is different.

Less optimistic, Dr. Ramsdell says, "I'm largely disappointed by these medications. Data from tests shows very small differences in outcomes between those who take the drugs and those who do not." He often recommends that patients try the medications but discontinue them if they see no impact. He warns that they can have numerous side effects.

Both physicians believe in the crucial role of meaningful behavior-based practices, as embodied by Silverado.

Silverado's normalization approach fights stigma. When those with dementia are nicely dressed and groomed, they feel confident about looking good and participating in appropriate programs. In turn, this enables the non-memory-impaired to relate to them better. In Silverado's surrounding communities, residents are seen practicing their putting skills with the pro at a local golf course, going to the theater, shooting pool and grabbing burgers at a pub, delivering hand-knitted blankets to a shelter for women and children, and walking Silverado's dogs around the neighborhood. This breaks down social barriers and shows that memory impairment need not isolate people from the world.

"Silverado treats each of its residents like a human being, not like someone with a disease," Dr. Dattoma said. "This approach is an important part of the solution to the issue of stigma."

Slipping her purse over one arm, Vic's mother, Alice, leaves her room headed to breakfast. She has only gone a few steps when Sonia intercepts her.

"Good morning, Alice," she exclaims. "How are you today?"

"Fine, thank you," Alice answers. "And you?"

"Just wonderful," Sonia replies. Reaching out to touch Alice's hand with affection, she adds, "I'm even better for seeing you."

Alice walks a short distance further and is again stopped, this time by Wilmer.

"Alice, how is your day going so far?" he asks.

"Very well," Alice says. "How are you?"

"Fantastic and happy that you are having a good day," Wilmer says. "Enjoy your breakfast."

What could be a short walk to Silverado's dining room ends up taking Alice considerably longer. It will be like this all day as caregivers, engagement specialists, culinary team members, housekeepers, and the executive director stop to greet her, and at times give her a hug.

Memory impaired and in her eighties, Alice has blossomed since moving into Silverado. She had lived with her son Vic for four years, but despite their loving efforts, her family could not provide this constantly positive atmosphere that is such a tonic for her.

Smiles, respect, and love are how Silverado fights stigma, and it's the way the rest of the world can overcome it too.

Chapter Five

Connecting with the Human Spirit

We do not believe in ourselves until someone reveals that deep inside us something is valuable, worth listening to, worthy of our trust, sacred to our touch. Once we believe in ourselves we can risk curiosity, wonder, spontaneous delight, or any experience that reveals the human spirit.

– Ralph Waldo Emerson

Jean slid under the hedge, cramming herself as far under the spiky branches as she could. Lying on her back, she grabbed fistfuls of leaves and piled them over her legs. Then, she dropped a last handful over her face. The moist leaves molded to her cheeks, her chin, and her eyelids.

It wasn't easy for Maryam to find her.

"Jean, why did you disappear on us?" she asked, kneeling down and gently brushing the leaves away.

"Police dogs were chasing me," Jean said. "The men with black masks were telling them to catch me. How dare they? How dare they come after me like this?"

Just after breakfast that morning, Jean had noticed several other Silverado residents walking with two of the community's dogs. It sparked a hallucination, and Jean fled out the nearest door, frantic to hide from her imagined pursuers.

Jean had memory impairment. For several years, her family doctor had waved off Jean's increasing lapses of recollection as "just old age." Until her condition was revealed in a startlingly public way.

The day before attending a political convention, 80-year-old Jean made it known she planned to make her entrance in a white winter suit, dressy white hat, and designer jewelry, in keeping with her customary regal style. But rather than arrive with studied panache, she burst into the meeting hall dressed in sweatpants and slippers, cradling a stuffed green frog in a Santa hat. Dashing over to a group of acquaintances, she exclaimed she was having car trouble. When they ran outside, they found her vehicle in the middle of the parking lot, engine running, all four doors open, and jewelry strewn across the back seat.

Convention organizers summoned an ambulance. In the emergency room, physicians diagnosed frontal-lobe dementia. Less prevalent than Alzheimer's disease, the condition can involve hallucinations, often accompanied by anger and aggression. When Jean left the hospital, she moved into Silverado.

Several days after she arrived, Jean grabbed a cane and smashed the Christmas tree in the lobby. Not having sufficiently made her point, she hurled a cup of hot coffee – saucer included – at a caregiver who stopped to chat with her. If Jean had been living almost any place other than Silverado, she would have quickly received a slew of tranquilizing medications.

But at Silverado, her outbursts were not viewed as senseless symptoms of memory impairment, but rather as one part of a complicated personality.

"We don't drug our residents to silence them," said Loren Shook. "We listen to them and observe what their bodies are expressing through gestures. By understanding how to connect with their spirit, we are able to provide the best care for them."

Who was Jean before she came to Silverado? She was a businesswoman, an owner of commercial buildings, the holder of a real estate license. Starting in her teens and throughout her life, Jean participated in a dizzying array of community groups, invariably ascending to their presidencies. These groups included a historical society, a town bicentennial committee, and various business and professional groups for women. As a child, she licked stamps and stuffed envelopes for presidential candidate Wendell Wilkie. Her passion for Republican politics was so fervent that she twice served as a delegate to the GOP presidential nominating convention. Following political news incessantly, she kept her television tuned to talk shows twenty-four hours a day. Jean owned 100 pairs of shoes and had collected 600 hats. She married five times. Those closest to her are quick to say she was never an easy person; they describe her as authoritative and controlling.

A few days after Jean's dash into Silverado's garden, Maryam, who is the resident engagement director at Jean's community, stopped by her room. She noticed that the shade on the lamp by Jean's bed was covered with jagged dark pink stripes with the hue and consistency of lipstick.

"Jean," Maryam asked, "did you do this?"

Jean nodded. "Look in the closet." Maryam opened the closet door. Inside, angry words had been scrawled on the walls in the same pink.

"To say the least, Jean's spirit was expressing itself," Maryam said a year later. "She had always been so independent, so strong. Now, she was angry because she had lost her authority and control. To provide the care that would be best for her, we would need to give that authority and control back to her. The way to do that was to involve Jean in more than the Silverado engagements themselves."

"We started by asking her to observe the classes and clubs we have for residents and to tell us if she thought there were ways they could be improved. I told her we needed someone with her experience."

Little by little, Jean became intrigued. As Jean began to assist, Maryam assigned her a desk in the engagement department and provided her with a name badge identical to those worn by the community staff.

These days, Jean sits in on interviews of potential employees for the engagement department. In addition, she creates binders of photos and information for suggested activities. She also runs the community's flower-arranging club. "Not every class runs smoothly," Maryam admits, "but many of them do."

As Jean's involvement with the program increased, her outbursts disappeared. Despite her memory impairment, a year after coming to Silverado Jean is able to reflect on her transition. "I rebelled because I felt my way of life was being taken away from me and that I was being held against my will. Running the classes gives me a sense of fulfillment. I can do something and be appreciated by others."

Jean no longer collects hats or shoes. She never watches the television in her room and she recently asked that it be taken out. She doesn't have time for it. "Working with flowers is more important to me now. When you look at a beautiful arrangement, you can't help but feel satisfied that you created it."

Her transformation has surprised and gratified her daughters, Teri and Linda.

"She has so much pleasure with the flower arranging," Teri said. "Maybe she's revisiting a part of her early identity before she became wrapped up in so many activities and politics."

Linda added, "For our mother, memory impairment hasn't meant the end of an active life. It's more like a new stage of life, one that has been tremendously satisfying."

Connecting with the spirit of someone with memory impairment is not a one-size-fits-all practice. It takes time, and it can be discouraging and frustrating in the meanwhile. With Jean, caregivers listened to what she had to say and were able to draw her out as they learned and interpreted her life story.

For Henry, the connection happened one morning as he watched workmen outside his window. When he had first come to Silverado, he barely spoke. Every time he was invited to join an engagement, he avoided eye contact, refusing to leave the chair by his bed. When staff brought breakfast on a tray, he turned away. Later, they would find it almost untouched.

One day, several Silverado residents and staff moved a small barn into the community's courtyard and began painting it. They were preparing for an event with a Western theme. After days of apathy, Henry was suddenly interested. He came outside, sat down, crossed one leg over another, and watched the activity for several hours, his face alert with an appraising expression.

Why did Henry's spirit come to life? Silverado staff members knew Henry had supervised his own company for many years. They thought he might respond to the bustle of a work site. So, when the barn needed to be painted, they made sure Henry would see the activity.

"For the next few days, we asked him if he would take his breakfast in the courtyard and keep an eye on what was going on," explained Carole, administrator of the community where he resides. "The change in Henry from that day on was enormous."

David is a chaplain with Silverado Hospice. Understanding how to connect with the spirit of the memory impaired wasn't obvious for him at the outset. Often, his very first meeting with the residents occurs when they can no longer open their eyes or speak. He remarks, "It's one thing to provide nursing care to the memory impaired at the end of life, but what does it mean to be a chaplain when a person no longer appears to be responsive? Being a chaplain involves communication."

Through his training and his experience at Silverado, David now maintains, "People in a remote state, whether a coma or deep dementia, are still people, and we can reach them." He often starts by matching his breathing to the patient's pace. After establishing a bond through this shared cadence, he adds words. "I can feel the rhythm of your breath. I can see that your eyes are moving under your eyelids. If it's all right with you, I would like to hold your hand for a while."

Time and again, David has seen how presence, focus, and touch spark a spiritual connection, which expresses itself through small, but compelling signs. One example was his contact with a man in the last stages of Parkinson's.

"As I held his hand, it had strong tremors from his disease. I began to talk to him about the transition from this life to the next. After a while, despite the tremors, I could feel that he was squeezing my hand. It was a powerful moment."

"Touching the spirit of the memory impaired at life's end has enriched me tremendously and given me a better understanding of myself," David says.

The inevitable downward progression of memory impairment is like a thief slipping into our lives and robbing us of the person we were and the people we knew. How is it possible that diseases affecting memory can change us in a positive way?

"I don't think people understand how nourishing it is to our minds and to our emotions to connect with another human spirit," Carole, the community administrator, said. "This connection is something we fundamentally need as human beings, but we're losing it in modern life. When I can focus on another person, when it's just the two of us communicating – regardless of whether we use words – it feeds every piece of my soul."

She added that she is thankful every day that Silverado's residents allow her to have this connection with them. "They do so much more for me than I could ever do for them."

Carole's work with the memory impaired has spanned two decades. She holds what many would consider a renegade view: that this disease, while heartbreaking, can also be liberating. Released from the inhibitions of social conventions, many Silverado residents try engaging in activities they would never have considered before. A man who rarely stepped into his kitchen at home joins the resident cooking club. A woman builds a bird-house, even though she used to think of herself as all thumbs. Add to that the resident who was always told she was tone-deaf and is now part of the community chorus. At Silverado, her spirit has the freedom to sing its song.

Chapter Six

The Power of Normal

Simply the thing that I am shall make me live.

– William Shakespeare

People walking into Silverado for the first time might be surprised to see a group of men in the living room drinking beer and watching a football game on television. But they wouldn't think twice if they saw the same thing in someone's home.

Silverado's view is that residents don't have to change what they normally like to do just because they've moved into a memory care community. In fact, not changing is central to Silverado's care. This practice is called "normalization." Bengt Nirje, the Swedish humanitarian and scholar who formulated the concept, defined the word with a poet's grace:

> *Normalization means… A normal rhythm of the day.*
>
> *You get out of bed in the morning…*
>
> *You get dressed*
>
> *And leave the house for school or work,*
>
> *You don't stay home…*
>
> *The day is not a monotonous 24 hours with every minute endless.*
>
> *You eat at normal times of the day and in a normal fashion…*

Not in bed, but at a table;

Not early in the afternoon for the convenience of the staff.

Normalization means...A normal rhythm of the week.

You live in one place,

Go to work in another,

And participate in leisure activities in yet another...

Normalization means...A normal rhythm of the year...

Seasonal changes bring with them a variety

Of types of food, work, cultural events, sports,

Leisure activities.

Just think...We thrive on seasonal changes.

Normalization means...Having a range of choices,

Wishes and desires respected and considered.

When Bengt Nirje was 32, the Swedish Red Cross sent him to Austria to assist Hungarian refugees who had fled their country's 1956 revolution and had been crowded into military barracks in a camp near Vienna. Later, he was sent to other camps in Europe where some World War II refugees had been living for more than a decade. In assessing these people groups and their living conditions, Nirje was deeply affected.

"This period taught me that when you are a refugee, you have a past that is gone and does not count in your new country. No one cares about you... nobody trusts you...you really know nothing about the future. Your situation is bleak, uncertain, and anonymous. Such a situation can create a very unhealthy climate and dark moods...there is no place for you, your family, or your few belongings. You have to be strong...but you can become mentally 'wounded' and socially handicapped."

Nirje's next assignment was to raise funds for children in Sweden who had cerebral palsy. The objective of the Red Cross was to move the youngsters out of large impersonal institutions into settings that were more like home. Nirje was struck by how these children's lives paralleled those of the refugees. Like the segregated refugees, "...they could not be certain where they were going, their present position was bleak, and they had very little power. They enjoyed no independence...and their state of dependence humiliated them."

The principle of normalization aims to refute the idea that people who have disabilities should be kept separate from society.

From all of his experiences, Nirje was learning the importance of independence and the right to self-determination. Thus began the development of his normalization concept. When a group of people is treated as less than normal because of physical, mental, or economic condition, their spirits wither. He determined that living with the same customs of society and with personal choices should be everyone's right.

In 1969, a United States presidential commission studied the living conditions of people with mental disabilities. Citing normalization, their landmark report brought fresh attention to the large facilities where many mentally handicapped Americans had been sent. What emerged was shocking: reports of people living nearly naked, soiled by their own waste, showered as a group by cold water from a hose, locked alone in barren rooms with only small barred windows for light.

As a result of this disclosure, a push began in the mental health profession to move developmentally disabled people out of the horrific institutions and into small group homes in cities and towns where they could become part of society.

At about the same time, psychologist Dr. Wolf Wolfensberger was extending Nirje's work on normalization to include other "devalued people."

As a child in Germany during World War II when bombs were falling in the cities, Wolfensberger was sent to the countryside for safety. Years later in the United States, he earned a Ph.D. in psychology, with a focus on developmental disability and special education. Writing over forty books and monographs and more than 250 chapters and articles, Dr. Wolfensberger earned worldwide renown as he focused on a question sparked by his own traumatic experience as a child in war time: How can people who are seemingly good do bad things to others?

Dr. Wolfensberger determined that the pattern begins when groups of people with similar traits (physical or mental impairment, nationality, race, or religion,) are devalued in the eyes of those considered normal. From there, it's all too easy to treat people in ways that would otherwise be unthinkable. This disregard can begin with simple acts of discourtesy. Left unchecked, it can slide downward with surprising speed to verbal, emotional, and physical abuse – even to deprivation of life itself.

Silverado is the only memory care organization founded on normalization, and its use grew directly from the work of Nirje and Wolfensberger.

At Silverado, you will never see a coloring book and crayons lying on a table in front of a silver-haired man. It's not dignified.

You won't spot a lady walking down the hall at three in the afternoon clad in bathrobe and slippers. It's not "normal."

You will not come across laundered undergarments piled immodestly on the top of a dresser. It's demeaning.

You won't see a hand-scrawled note taped to the wall by a bed that says, "He needs toileting frequently." It's not respectful.

At Silverado, you will see football fans gathered in front of a game with brews and chips, sharing a lifelong Sunday afternoon passion.

You'll notice ladies dressed in the daytime attire they've always worn. When they head out from their rooms to participate in programs and activities, they carry their purses with them, as any woman might upon leaving her house.

When you visit residents in their rooms, you'll find that intimate apparel is tucked out of sight and the walls are free of demeaning notes. In their place

As you walk down the halls of Silverado, "memory boxes" – lovely cabinets filled with memorabilia of many lives and many special people – surround you. are family pictures, cherished artwork, souvenirs from special trips, and other meaningful items that represent the arc of normal living. Memory boxes just outside residents' rooms hold mementos testifying to individual interests and achievements. Gold records shine in the display by the room of a music industry executive. A baseball mitt and trophies are the cherished possessions of a resident who made a name for himself in minor league ball and might have reached the big leagues if not for a bum elbow.

Disease of the brain may have brought on a host of changes, but it has not sent people back to childhood. At times, people seeking positions as caregivers at Silverado will say, "I treat the people I care for the way I would treat my own children." While they mean well, it reflects the common attitude in the senior living profession that a memory-impaired person is childlike.

Silverado's adherence to normalization is so stringent that teams of employees conduct normalization audits; staff from one Silverado community will visit another. They devote an entire day to touring, making sure no aspect of operations or resident care has strayed from normality.

"We do this from a constructive criticism standpoint," said a resident engagement director who recently participated in an inspection. "When you work in the same community every day, you need to bring in a fresh set of eyes to make sure nothing has been overlooked."

For nearly two decades after her husband passed away, Maria lived by herself in an apartment. Her three grown children stopped in nearly every day, enabling her to continue the routine that has been central to her adult life: cooking meals and chatting in the Spanish language of her native Argentina. As Maria neared eighty, her family noticed changes in her behavior, which were ultimately diagnosed as symptoms of memory impairment. She moved into a senior living community where the staff tried to involve her in sing-alongs and games with other residents.

"It was a nice place and the people there worked hard to get her to participate, but she wasn't interested," her son Al recalled. Maria cried often and became restless, unable to sit still for more than a few minutes.

After her condition declined to the point of hospitalization, Maria's family brought her to Silverado. From interviews with Maria and her family, Silverado's staff realized how important meal preparation had been to her life. It represented normal living for Maria; participating in sing-along activities and conversing in English did not. Maria had lost her normal.

Once Silverado's staff understood what was missing from Maria's life, they restored it. The culinary staff, which included several Spanish speakers, invited her to help out in the kitchen. Maria accepted the offer and began setting the tables for dinner.

In the ensuing months, she happily took on more responsibilities. Now, she prepares the tables for all three daily meals. She chops ingredients and garnishes plates, chatting in Spanish with her kitchen colleagues all the while.

To those who work alongside Maria in the kitchen, she is a teammate and friend, a normal part of the team. To others in her Silverado community, she's a smiling and active presence, busy with her daily routines. Her memory impairment is just another part of what makes her an individual, as does her ability to speak Spanish, her love of cooking, and many other personal traits.

No one can remember the last time Maria cried.

"My mother has returned to her old ways," her son Al said. "She has adopted a second family to care for and has been given back the lifestyle that mattered to her. She has purpose again."

That is the power of normal.

Chapter Seven

A Different Point of View

Whatever course you decide upon, there is always someone to tell you that you are wrong. There are always difficulties arising, which tempt you to believe that your critics are right. To map out a course of action and follow it to an end requires courage.

– Ralph Waldo Emerson

A small boy and a dog crossed a field under a black blanket of sky scattered with pinpricks of starlight and a crescent slit of moon. It was the kind of darkness only possible in a place many miles from street lamps and passing cars. Though Loren and his hound Duke had barely enough light to see where they were going, they knew the way.

He was only five, but every day Loren and the dog walked nearly half a mile to feed 500 chickens. In a family that raised fowl for a living in rural Washington State, Loren's duty was to come straight home after kindergarten and head for the coops.

On this day, the temptation to join the other children on the playground after school had been too great. When he finally returned home, it was dark. His mother gave him a long look and said nothing. While Loren was washing his hands for dinner, his father came home from his job at the feed mill. Calmly, she informed her husband the chickens had not been fed. Turning to Loren, his father said in a tone not unkind but firm, "Son, you have to feed those chickens, right now."

As Loren took his jacket off the hook by the door, his father disappeared into the bedroom to change his coveralls and his mother turned back to the soup bubbling on the stove. Loren stepped outside and picked up the flashlight lying on a worktable under the eaves of the house. Duke appeared at his side.

Loren looked into the inky night and swallowed hard. He clicked the flashlight on, pointed its thin beam forward, and began walking. The darkness turned hedges into gargoyles. Rustling squirrels became monsters' footsteps. Duke's panting was the only familiar sound in the alien landscape.

After what felt like the longest walk of his life, he and Duke reached the coops and Loren made quick work of feeding the chickens. Then, the pair set off on the frightening trek back to the farmhouse. When they arrived, Duke slipped off to the barn and Loren went into the kitchen. His father was sitting at the table, his mother ladling the soup into his bowl. "I got the chickens fed, Dad," Loren said. His father nodded an indication for Loren to wash his hands and come to the table.

Loren and his father never talked about that night, not even when Loren grew into an adult who could question being sent alone on such a walk at the age of five. He remembers, "I learned a lesson that night about responsibility, what you owe your family. When you have duties, you don't shirk them."

Loren's father had always dreamed of owning his own chicken farm. When Loren was a year old, his family moved from Iowa to Washington and the family bought a farm that was a boy's paradise: two dozen acres of pasture, hills, trees, and a sprawling house. To supplement their farming income, his parents took jobs they considered temporary to tide them over until the chicken business grew sufficiently. But by the time Loren was five, the dream had failed and the family was forced to put the farm up for sale. Loren hid the for-sale sign in the woods, thinking it would stop the transaction. It didn't.

His mother's brother, Bernard Hambleton, offered the penniless family employment at Fairfax Hospital, a psychiatric sanitarium he and his wife, Marion, owned near Seattle. In addition, he let them stay in a tiny house on the grounds. At night, Loren and his older brother slept on two small beds in one room while his parents slept on a fold-out sofa in another. His father was the maintenance man at the sanitarium, his mother an aide and cook. They also began raising chickens on contract in coops scattered throughout the region. As a first-grader, Loren was responsible for 3,000 chickens, the number doubling by the time he was in third grade. Four years later when his father was often too ill to work, his flock grew to 45,000 chickens.

Decades later, it wasn't the poultry Loren would remember. He can still close his eyes and sense the sting in his nose and throat from waste piled three feet high in the chicken houses. He can remember the ache in his shoulders and back from hauling tons of the smelly matter out of the coops in a wheelbarrow during seasonal cleanings.

The failure of the family farm hung over Loren's father. As anxiety seared ulcers into his stomach, there were still many days he couldn't get out of bed for work. So when Loren was fifteen, he took a job at the sanitarium to help care for the animals, work in the gardens, and generally help out.

Later, he also served as a companion for the patients. The Hambletons believed that productive work was important in the treatment of a wide variety of psychiatric disorders.

As such, Loren often asked patients to work with him while he went about his duties at the hospital. It was not unusual for Loren to drive the hospital's truck to the feed store with a thirty-year-old man with suicidal tendencies sitting next to him. When the teen received orders to wax the hospital's first floor, his helpmate was an heir to an old New England family; he was under treatment for explosive rages.

Loren had never been formally trained regarding patient care. The staff assumed he would figure it out, and he did. Adopting a nonchalant and friendly tone, he would invite his charges to "help me out with some stuff today." He learned the art of watching without being noticed and of discerning unvoiced thoughts, desires, and anger.

Later, Loren would say, "If you could understand what the patients were saying with their eyes and body language, you could anticipate what they were about to do, even if they didn't say a word."

Always busy, Loren added to his load by starting a veal business with several classmates. He also found time for school sports. Despite his family's troubles with money and his father's poor health, his parents encouraged his athletics from Little League through college. Loren played football, baseball, and basketball, and was especially drawn to running track.

As he neared adulthood, Loren was sprinting in other ways: he was going to make something of himself. For a long time, he thought he would be a cattle rancher. Throwing himself into this endeavor, he worked hard during summers at a nearby ranch and immersed himself in anything he could read on the subject.

By the end of high school, however, farmers in the area were struggling to survive, an ominous harbinger for even the most ambitious rancher. He read that starting a cattle ranch required a half-million dollar investment. No matter how many hours he worked at his various jobs, reaching that amount appeared impossible.

When his uncle suggested using his experience at the sanitarium as the basis for a career as a psychiatric hospital administrator, Loren followed his advice. He pursued a business degree, first at a community college and then at the University of Washington, all the while working as many as forty hours a week at Fairfax Hospital. Further, he bought out his friends' interests in the veal business, shouldering the entire workload, and started raising purebred Black Angus cattle.

When Loren was a junior at the university in 1972, the Hambletons retired, selling Fairfax Hospital to CPC (Community Psychiatric Centers), a company that operated psychiatric hospitals in several states. A variety of corporate brass with the firm visited Fairfax Hospital during the transition to the new ownership. Loren had the job of picking up the executives at the airport. At the wheel one day, he told the CEO that he planned a career in psychiatric hospital administration. The CEO offered Loren a position as assistant administrator at one of its California hospitals when he graduated.

A year later, Loren arrived at CPC's headquarters for the administration-training program. When a vice president emerged from a corner office and told Loren he was being sent to the purchasing department, Loren refused to be reassigned. After a tense standoff, the executive yielded, and Loren joined the training program alongside two new hires who were fifteen years older and had previous administration experience. Several weeks into the course, he was given the job. The other two could not keep up with him.

Loren was only twenty-two years old, fresh-faced and lean. Many made the mistake of assuming he was the overgrown kid he appeared to be. However, after six months as an assistant administrator, Loren was promoted to an administrator's position at a larger CPC hospital. There, he was tested in an environment riddled with operational and procedural problems. Loren took the helm and the problems were resolved.

Because of his success in that assignment, Loren was dispatched to lead the CPC hospitals with the worst records: patient numbers falling, staff members ignoring procedures, and adolescent patients out of control. Invariably, he turned the facilities around.

"At first, hospital staffs would doubt me," Loren said years later, "but I've always had the gift of a command presence. When I was growing up, I did well with bulls. When you have a big animal like that, you need to be able to handle it, or it's going to handle you. Once I got the cooperation of the staff, they began to understand how my methods worked."

People who knew Loren during his career at CPC describe him tactfully as "probably more hard-nosed and aggressive in his focus than he is now."

Likely, those hospital staffers never met anyone who worked the way Loren did. He grew up never having a day off. It was no different now. When Loren took on a new hospital, he slept there most nights before relocating his family to the area. He lived alongside the patients, the same way he had at Fairfax Hospital. Schizophrenics, the profoundly depressed, the phobia-ridden – they were his fellow residents. So were elders with ebbing memories and unpredictable moods. He never considered that psychiatric patients were anything other than human beings who happen to have illnesses of the mind. His purpose in living among them went beyond bringing the hospital in line with CPC's rulebook. He was there to raise the facility to the best level of care.

Loren did not stop running during his years with CPC. Once he fixed the problem assigned to him, filling the time with more work was natural. He developed new programs in marketing and patient care and he attended independent study graduate programs in hospital administration. At the University of Saskatchewan in Saskatoon, Loren studied the intricacies of Canada's health care system. At the University of Minnesota, he taught himself the ins and outs of property acquisition and hospital development. All the while, Loren was pushing CPC's brass to expand the company. Ultimately, Loren charged all the way to the top of the corporate ladder and became president and chief operating officer of CPC's worldwide operations. When Loren first joined CPC, the firm had six mental health hospitals. By the end of Loren's 20-year tenure, it was operating 50 psychiatric hospitals, over 100 renal dialysis units, and a sub-acute medical surgical hospital business. Newly married in his early twenties when he began, he was a father in his forties when he left CPC in 1993.

> Vascular dementia is widely considered the second most common type of dementia.

Asked why he walked away from the top post at a successful company, he explains, "The psychiatric industry was changing. Due to the influence of some less-than-ethical operators, managed care was given free rein to reduce cost, which in large part was done by denying care. I called it the

1-800-JUST SAY NO line." He believed the trend would not alter. While he was proud of CPC's operations, he didn't want to be part of the industry anymore.

Doing nothing was unthinkable for the man who had worked every day since childhood. He couldn't shut the door and walk away from those he had assisted, befriended, and lived with for so long, and he realized that one group needed him the most. They were the people with Alzheimer's disease, vascular dementia, Parkinson's, and other conditions that robbed memory.

Parkinson's disease is a degenerative neurological disorder of the brain related to a depletion of a neurotransmitter called dopamine.

Loren understood that psychiatric hospitals weren't the right place for them. They were not mentally ill. They had diseases of the brain that produced symptoms, which at times appeared to be psychiatric in nature, but were actually biological. With rare exceptions, their conditions followed six or seven robust decades of building families, careers, and friendships. Then, they lost everything they loved, and the world became an alien place. When Loren's own father needed care in his later years for a non-operable brain tumor, which caused severe dementia-like symptoms, grim hospitals and nursing homes were still his only option.

Every experience in Loren's life had built up to this moment. After his years at CPC, Loren was prepared to risk everything he had to save these people.

Chapter Eight

Two Minds, One Vision

Vision is the art of seeing what is invisible to others.

– Jonathan Swift

Of all the experts who stepped up to the podium that day, only one was a layperson. Yet he drew the largest crowd. In a packed room of physicians, nurses, social workers, and psychologists, many in the crowd had to lean against the walls to hear Steve Winner, a revolutionary in Alzheimer's care. He urged the audience:

"Get the memory impaired up, dressed, and out of their rooms first thing in the morning.

Untie the straps and belts that confine their bodies.

Stop giving drugs that dull their psyches.

Ban balloon toss, block stacking and other childish pastimes.

Fill their days with art classes, music jams, and other activities that matter.

Haul away the vinyl couches, the linoleum tables, the metal seats.

Move in fabric sofas and chairs, colorful curtains and paintings.

Swing the doors wide open to welcome dogs, cats, birds, and children.

Cheer as these people come back to life."

With Steve's closing remarks, those attending the 1995 Alzheimer's Symposium at the University of California San Diego stood to roar their approval. Dozens swarmed him with questions.

One man sat writing page after page of notes. Deep in thought, Loren Shook stayed seated long after Steve had finished. Loren had never met Steve. He hadn't even heard of him. Since leaving his position at CPC, Loren had been determined to open a different place from those he had seen, one where the memory impaired could live up to their potential and enjoy life. He had never known there was someone else out there who thought the way he did.

In his youth, Steve Winner had a fleeting brush with memory impairment. An aunt developed Alzheimer's disease and moved into a nursing home. Steve visited her from time to time to break her daily routine of doing nothing. Only much later did Steve understand how stultifying her last years had been. The realization troubled him.

Steve entered the University of Maryland planning to major in business. Soon after the school year began, he found a part-time job to help pay college expenses. The position as caregiver in a group home for the mentally disabled required him to work weekends, sleeping at the group home on Friday and Saturday nights. Weekdays would be free to study and attend classes.

His first evening on the job, Steve made sure all the residents had turned in, and then he retired to the staff bedroom. In the early hours of the morning, he was jolted awake by loud conversation coming from the living room. As the vehement voices rose and fell, Steve pulled on his bathrobe and padded down the steps to find out why so many residents were up so early.

"When I walked into the room, I discovered just one person was there," Steve recalled. "He was talking in eight different voices." Not having been trained how to handle such a situation, he took a deep breath and went with instinct.

"Come on, William," he said gently. "It's really time for you to be asleep." William nodded, stood up from the sofa, and allowed Steve to walk him back upstairs to his room.

The experience got Steve off to an awkward start. For the first few weeks, he was uncomfortable around the residents. Gradually, as he lived among them and heard their life stories, he began knowing them as individuals.

Lois, for example, had only stubble on her scalp when she moved into the group home. She had been exiled as a child to a large state-run institution where it was standard practice to shave everyone's head. She was also forcibly sterilized during her teen years, destroying forever her dream of having a family.

Steve never forgot how Lois talked about this trauma, how she alternately sobbed and raged over it, as would any woman grieving and struggling to come to terms with personal tragedy. Her mental disability did not make her any less female, less human, or less susceptible to pain.

Over the next few years, Steve watched Lois blossom in the group home setting. She grew her hair to her shoulders. Later, she got a job, moved into an apartment, fell in love, and married.

Steve discovered that he was drawn to the people of the group home; he connected with their dreams, thoughts, and talents. Further, he was able to help them to carve their places in the world and to build lives filled with purpose and pleasure. Discarding business as a career, Steve declared his major in behavioral psychology.

Graduating from college, Steve turned his passion into his career. He landed a position directing programs for the developmentally disabled in Virginia. At the same time, he began studying for a master's degree in rehabilitative counseling. He started his course work with a two-week session on normalization at Syracuse University led by one of its pioneers, Dr. Wolf

Wolfensberger. In that setting, Steve began to consider in a wider context what he had learned at the group home. He listened raptly as Dr. Wolfensberger and other professors explained how society can identify particular groups of people as "apart from the norm" and how placing less value on them can lead to humiliation, mistreatment, and deprivation of rights – up to and including their right to live.

Decades later, Steve says, "Understanding how social and political practices can deny the validity of individuals changed me in a fundamental way."

As part of his studies, he visited large state institutions for the mentally handicapped to collect research for Dr. Wolfensberger. Lois and other residents at the group home had told Steve about these places. In fact, many of his residents had come from these institutions as part of an early wave in the movement to bring the mentally handicapped into the mainstream of life.

Hearing about them did not prepare him for seeing them.

"They were horror shows."

Long afterwards, what he witnessed remained sharp in his memory. "The staff would unlock big heavy double doors and you would walk through into the wards. You would find people half-naked, sometimes sitting in their feces. They would be crying, yelling, rocking – and no one was paying any attention. I was in shock that human beings could be treated this way."

The normalization theory of Bengt Nirje and Wolf Wolfensberger became Steve's holy grail. Living in the group home, he regarded his residents as individuals with worth, not as social outcasts. But he understood the continuing peril they would be in until society as a whole embraced them.

In 1980, Steve moved to Southern California, where he became program director for the developmentally disabled and psychiatric wings of Georgian Court, a private health care facility. Years later, when Georgian Court changed hands, the new owners converted it to a geriatric care center. Steve never planned to work in geriatrics, but he stayed on at Georgian Court while he searched for a job in rehabilitation for the mentally disabled.

It was difficult. He recoiled at how the new management at Georgian Court cared for its residents. They were kept clean and fed; their medications were given as needed. But the staff barely knew their names, let alone anything about them as individuals. The patients spent their days tied into wheelchairs lining Georgian Court's hallways, backs to the wall and eyes looking blankly into space.

"Couldn't we at least turn the wheelchairs so that people face each other, so they have eye contact, maybe even talk to each other?" Steve asked at a management meeting. The executives blinked, baffled. Their puzzlement soon turned to irritation as the young interloper offered more ideas in subsequent gatherings. After six months, Steve left Georgian Court to direct a large organization of residences and rehabilitation programs for the mentally disabled.

Three years passed and the work he thought he would never do again tapped him on the shoulder. The previous owner of Georgian Court was on the phone. He now worked for a company planning to convert a skilled nursing facility into a residence dedicated to Alzheimer's care. Called Parkside Special Care Center, it would be the first of its kind in Southern California. If Steve were interested in becoming its administrator, the company would pay for him to visit the best Alzheimer's care centers around the country. He would then be free to design his own program for Parkside.

At first, Steve dismissed the idea; the career he had trained for was working with the developmentally disabled. Still, he had trouble putting the offer out of his mind; he always regretted his powerlessness to help the elderly residents he left behind at Georgian Court. This call out of the blue was a chance to make things right, if not for the people at Georgian Court, then at least for others facing a similar plight.

He took the job.

When Steve embarked on his first round of visits to Alzheimer's care facilities across the United States, he assumed he would return with pages of notes on practices to emulate. But his notepad remained empty. In all the facilities he visited, he might as well have been walking the halls of Georgian Court all over again. He saw the same rows of wheelchairs along hallways, the same lifeless stares by seniors lost in inactivity and anonymity. If these places were the gold standard in memory care, things were going to have to change.

So far, Steve's field of developmental disability care was the only one using the principles of normalization, but Steve was convinced they would serve equally well in Alzheimer's care. After all, the memory impaired who were confined to nursing homes lost their social status just as the mentally disabled did, and they were exiled from the normality of the rest of the world, which considered them less than human.

Steve set out to transform care for the memory impaired by restoring their normal.

Parkside Special Care Center had tile floors, vinyl-covered furniture bolted to the floor, employees in white uniforms, and countless televisions blaring non-stop in front of motionless residents. If Steve were to reshape Parkside to his own vision of normalization, everything about the place would need to change, including the attitudes of the staff. The key to transforming Parkside would be having everyone on the same page. They needed to understand this was not a "warehouse" for the memory impaired; it was their home. So when Steve arrived at Parkside for his first day on the job, his golden retriever Jasper was at his side – because "there's nothing more normal than having a dog around the house."

While pet therapy would become an accepted practice in senior care in subsequent decades, it was unheard of the day Jasper trotted through the front hallway. Animals were considered a sanitation hazard, which could raise the eyebrows of state inspectors sky high. But in the interests of those in his care, he was more immediately concerned about the staff.

Several studies have shown health benefits of people's interaction with pets both mentally and physically. The pets at Silverado communities offer unconditional love of all residents.

Lori had been working in Parkside's medical records department for two years before Steve arrived. "He had a totally different vision of what Parkside should be, and we took his changes as an insult to our work," she said.

In meeting after meeting, Steve laid out his ideas to the incredulous employees. The floors would be redone in a pattern the residents could follow to encourage them to walk. Colorful wallpaper, plush furniture, and leafy plants would turn the atmosphere from clinical to inviting. More dogs and cats would join Jasper, along with tanks of fish and cages of birds.

Further, staff would keep the office doors open. "If residents wander in, invite them to sit down," Steve said. "Your office is a room in their home. They have as much right to go there as you do."

Residents would wear regular clothing during the day, rather than bathrobes and slippers. "We will need to call their families and ask them to bring in more of their clothes."

All beds would be made by 9:30 a.m., "because it's not normal to leave a bed unmade until the afternoon." Steve would pitch in to help and so should the other managers if it looked like the deadline might not be met. "And unless the residents are choosing to watch television, we'll turn the TVs off and get people involved in something meaningful."

Steve's changes alarmed Pat, the activities director. She had trained diligently for her work and she prided herself on it. Seeing she was upset, Steve sat down with her for a private conversation.

"Pat, think about what you like to do with your friends," Steve said. "When you get together, do you toss balloons? Do you stack blocks? Do you look at calendars and remind each other what the date is? It may be a well-intentioned effort to reorient the memory impaired to reality, but it simply causes confusion and stress. And how important is it that any of us knows today's date?"

She was silent for a few minutes. She had to admit it made sense, but it contradicted everything she had been taught. When Steve asked Pat to design the new engagement program, the prospect terrified her. "I resigned three times in the first six months, but Steve always told me I couldn't leave, that the residents needed me, that he needed me."

Soon, Parkside began to offer a program of activities unprecedented for those with memory impairment. Groups formed for residents to enjoy music, art, travel, and movies. Male residents were invited to put on ties and take part in men's club. Steve used his own money to buy ties for men who didn't have them.

Many employees left. "Those who stayed discovered new meaning in their work," Lori, the medical records staffer, said. "When I finally grasped what Steve was doing, I had more enthusiasm. Before, the people at Parkside were patients, not individuals I could get to know. I saw that when you give them the opportunity to engage more, they do!"

Each day brought a gratifying surprise. Staff members learned that many residents considered incontinent were not. They required assistance getting to the restroom and they might not have had the verbal skills to ask for help, but they communicated their need through body language. Once staff identified its meaning, it was easy to understand and to escort them to the bathroom when needed. Liberation from the humiliation of incontinence was a powerful tonic for these residents.

Steve constantly had to convince state inspectors that Parkside wasn't breaking rules; it was setting new standards of care. In less than a year, Parkside was transformed from a nursing home like any other into a sought-after establishment where families actually wanted their loved ones to reside. A waiting list developed. Within three years, Parkside's owners purchased a second nursing home for Steve to transform and manage.

Suddenly, Alzheimer's care experts from around the country wanted to see this revolution for themselves. Conference organizers sought Steve as a speaker. He appeared at the White House Conference on Aging. By the time Steve stepped up to the podium at the Alzheimer's Symposium in San Diego, he had been leading this movement for a decade.

In the three years before seeing Steve's presentation, Loren Shook had spent nearly all his waking hours researching Alzheimer's care. With the intention of starting an organization dedicated to caring for people with memory disorders, he had read every medical journal he could get his hands on, visited facilities with memory-impairment units, and peppered Alzheimer's experts with questions.

The odyssey had been frustrating. Touted nursing homes turned out to be nothing more than the usual "stinky, warehouse-like places where the managers counted the peas on residents' plates to make sure they weren't exceeding their budgets." He wanted to liberate the memory impaired from this, not condemn them to it. For too long, Alzheimer's patients had been written off as afflicted, incapacitated cases without hope. Loren knew them as people with interests, desires, and potential.

To help with the complex financial and real estate issues involved in launching the company he envisioned, Loren had enlisted longtime CPC colleague Jim Smith. Both men knew the organization would only come to life the way they envisioned if they could find the right person to lead resident care – someone who would smile in agreement when Loren talked about providing meaningful lives to people with memory impairment. So far, everyone they had interviewed had looked puzzled at best – and aghast at worst – when Loren described his plans.

Chapter Nine

The Dream Takes Shape

And above all, watch with glittering eyes the whole world around you, because the greatest secrets are always hidden in the most unlikely places. Those who don't believe in magic will never find it.

– Roald Dahl

Two men came into Parkside Special Care Center, one of them claiming to be searching for a place to care for his aging mother who had Alzheimer's disease.

Wearing jackets and no ties, they were trying hard to look casual. As Steve Winner showed the pair around Parkside, they fired questions at him, jotting his answers on pads encased in leather bindings.

Their manner and the depth of their inquiries about Parkside's services didn't square with normal behavior. As family members searched for suitable living arrangements for the memory impaired, emotion and uncertainty often overwhelmed them. Many were still struggling to comprehend basic facts about the disease that was slowly changing their loved one.

When the two men said they also wanted to visit Lo-Har Lodge, the other memory care center Steve oversaw, Steve guessed they were state inspectors hoping to snag Parkside and Lo-Har in a bureaucratic trap. For years regulators had been visiting him to challenge the two centers' unusual memory care programs.

Steve played along with the ruse.

After he finished escorting the men around both Parkside and Lo-Har Lodge, the two asked to meet with him privately. Steve took a deep breath and got ready for the blow. Bring it on, State of California. I'm ready.

Showing them into his office, he left the door open. "Parkside is the residents' home," he explained to his visitors. "They can go anywhere they wish, even here. If you don't want anyone to hear us, keep your voices down." Both men made another note as they settled into chairs facing Steve's desk.

The man whose mother had Alzheimer's disease – or so he said – leaned forward.

"We're starting an assisted living community for people with memory impairment," Loren Shook said. "We've searched far and wide for the right person to take charge of resident care. We both agree you're the person we've been looking for. Will you join us?"

Steve drew back in surprise. Then he smiled and said, "Thank you, but I'm happy right where I am."

Loren leaned in closer. Beside him, Jim Smith sat forward too. Then Loren began to describe his vision of a place where people with memory impairment would thrive.

Steve had never seen Loren before. He had never heard of him. He sat silently as the stranger voiced Steve's own thoughts, feelings, and dreams. When Loren finished speaking, Steve asked the only question that came to his mind.

"Will you have pets?"

"Yes, we love pets," Loren said. "We're going to have a lot of them."

"How many is a lot?"

"We're not putting any limit on the number and we're going to have every kind of pet you can imagine. Come to work with us and you can help us with pets."

All three men laughed. The ice broke. They spent several hours comparing ideas and spinning scenarios. Anyone glancing into Steve's office would have thought these guys were the best of buddies.

"What are you going to call your company?" Steve asked.

"Silverado Senior Living," Loren and Jim told him. It was Loren's idea. He was naming it after the Silverado Resort and Country Club in California's Napa Valley. The resort offered both tennis and golf, and a host of other activities and many amenities.

"They have something for everyone in the family to enjoy, regardless of age or interests," Loren said. "That is exactly how it's going to be at our community; it will be for everyone – residents and visitors, kids and adults alike."

When Loren and Jim rose to leave, they asked Steve to think about their offer. "Don't decide right now. Just take some time to consider what we discussed."

Steve had no intention of accepting. Nearly a decade had passed since he revolutionized care for people with Alzheimer's disease at Parkside Special Care Center. He had since brought the same changes to Lo-Har Lodge. When he closed his eyes, he could see each of the hundreds of residents he had known over the years. He remembered the moment an activity, a friendship, the laughter of a child, or the warmth of a pet brought an individual to life. How could he even consider leaving a place that was so much a part of him? But in the days that followed, he found himself thinking about the way Loren spoke. Steve had never met anyone who had reflected his own mind and sentiments in the purest passion the way Loren did.

A few weeks later, Steve fished Loren's card out of his desk and called him. He scheduled an appointment with Loren and Jim at their office in Orange

County, California. The three men squeezed their chairs together in the small space and again talked for several hours. Not long after that meeting, he called Loren and Jim and told them he would come aboard. "I went with my gut," Steve said.

For the next year, Steve held two jobs. Keeping his position as administrator at Parkside and Lo-Har during the day, he took the time to train his replacement. Working nights with Loren and Jim, he planned Silverado's resident care program. The owners of Parkside and Lo-Har understood what he was doing: the man who had designed their revolutionary memory care programs wanted to stand before an empty frame again and fill it with his vision.

During that time, Silverado Senior Living existed only in the minds of the three men. Loren and Jim were searching for a building, perhaps a skilled nursing facility or mental health hospital, to turn into their first memory care community.

One day, Steve received the call he had been expecting for twelve months: "Give your notice," Loren said. "We've got the place." Steve wrapped up his work at Parkside and Lo-Har Lodge and hugged residents and staff good-bye. Shortly after Steve turned in his keys, Loren called again. The deal had fallen through. Steve spent anxious days regretting what he thought could be the biggest mistake of his life.

Then one afternoon, as Steve was working in Loren and Jim's tiny office, the two strode in and said the deal was back on. Silverado was taking possession of the property that day. The three of them needed to get there as fast as possible. They piled into Steve's car and headed south to a nursing home in Escondido, California where Silverado would take shape.

"It's a pit," Loren told Steve as he maneuvered through heavy traffic. "It can accommodate 110 people. Right now, there are only twenty. It has a bad reputation; it's been through two bankruptcies." Loren described the cracks crisscrossing the floors, lamps languishing with burnt-out bulbs, knee-high weeds sprouting in the backyard, chairs and sofas so worn that "you'd fall through if you actually sat down," and a staff that won't look anyone in the eye. As the three men drove, dark clouds overhead opened and unexpected hail began to pound the highway. They pulled under an overpass to wait it out. "I hope this isn't an omen," Steve said, his apprehension apparent behind the joke.

The facility certainly didn't meet the criteria the new owners had set for their dream location, but after months of searching and fruitless negotiations, they felt it was now or never. They would have to make this work.

For Loren, more was riding on this endeavor than just his dream. He had convinced a private equity firm to invest in the project. He and Jim had staked a great deal of their own money, and Loren was also placing personal financial guarantees on his new company. Those around him at the time say he never displayed anything but confidence.

When the three arrived at the nursing home, the administrator stormed down the dark hall toward them. She hurled a ring of keys at them as she passed and snarled, "Here. It's all yours now." She slammed the front door on her way out. A moment later, they heard a car start and peel out of the parking lot.

Coming into the half-lit lobby, they needed a few moments for their eyes to adjust. "Wait, where are the couch and the chairs?" Jim asked. Loren scanned the area. The reception room furniture had vanished. Decrepit as it had been, its absence made the place ghostly.

Hearing a faint noise, they pushed open a door marked "Dining Room." They found residents sitting around linoleum tables, wraith-like and silent. Many were in wheelchairs, their faces turned down to their laps. The sound they heard came from a corner of the room where an employee was shuffling tableware in a plastic bin.

A few residents were picking at their food, but most ignored it. Loren, Jim, and Steve approached the tables. The plate in front of each person held yellowing pieces of lettuce and a small scoop of macaroni salad. Steve drew in his breath sharply. He leaned down beside the resident nearest to him and gently said: "Hi, I'm Steve. Is this all you're having for dinner?" The woman didn't respond. He stood and pushed his way through double doors leading to the kitchen. A man in a dingy jacket was leaning against a counter.

In his fury, Steve didn't introduce himself. "What are you serving?" he demanded. "Do you have anything decent for the residents to eat, any meat, anything with flavor?"

"We stopped feeding them meat a long time ago. The owners ran out of money," he said in his defense. "We buy stale bread in bulk. A lot of nights, we pour canned gravy over it and serve it to them as meat loaf."

Steve pivoted and strode back to the dining room to Loren and Jim. The three agreed this was not going to be the first meal on their watch. Loren kept an eye on things while Steve and Jim drove to the nearest McDonald's. They brought back bagfuls of hamburgers, chicken nuggets, and french fries for the residents.

The fragrance emanating from the paper sacks had a powerful effect. Residents who had seemed barely awake as they slumped around the tables began stretching their hands out for the food. They smiled, some spoke. Despite the sorry surroundings, the meal took on the air of a picnic.

Steve arranged to bring supplies from Parkside Special Care Center to tide over the residents until he could order supplies. He also brought a small team of long-time employees who were eager to assist Steve in shaping his new venture. He had left on excellent terms; the owners were happy to help.

Lori, the medical records staffer from Parkside said, "There was nothing we wouldn't do for him." In those early days at Silverado, only the position of chef was available to Lori. So she learned how to cook and how to operate all the kitchen equipment. With recipes from her mother, she multiplied the quantities by ten. (Her cinnamon rolls became a resident favorite.) Since Silverado could not afford to hire a dishwasher until occupancy reached forty residents, Lori also handled that task.

While Steve and a handful of employees focused on resident care, Loren and Jim set about renovating the place. Comfortable furniture, colorful paint and wallpaper, and sparkling cleanliness were priorities. So were flowers, walking paths, and a playground for youngsters who visited. As they installed a chandelier in the dining room, the dreary room became a bright, inviting place where people lingered after meals to talk. Even Loren, Jim, and Steve were surprised when seven residents who had once needed assistance at mealtime began to eat on their own from the sheer pleasure and energy of being in that room.

Ben was Silverado's first official new resident. Husky and over six feet tall, he had lost little of the strength that powered his college football career decades earlier. Ben came to Silverado from the hospital where he had angrily assaulted nurses and orderlies. As a result, his hands and feet were tied down to the gurney that brought him in. His wife walked beside him weeping. Silverado agreed to accept Ben in spite of his violence. If he lashed out here and hurt someone, his wife wouldn't know where to turn next, because no other senior living community would take him. Steve did his best to reassure her: "Silverado is his home now. Let's focus on getting him well."

Observing Ben and reviewing his history, Steve and the staff members were certain he was in physical pain. The abundance of psychotropic drugs in his body was aggravating his condition. No longer able to communicate through words in a way those around him could understand, he was expressing his anguish through punches and kicks.

Freeing Ben from his restraints, the Silverado staff placed a mattress on the floor so he wouldn't hurt himself if he fell from his bed. They adjusted his pain medication and cut back on other drugs as well. Then, they introduced him to Cassie, the community's resident Labrador retriever. Steve still smiles as he recalls the delicate dance between the two. At first, Cassie would walk up to Ben as he reclined on his bed and push her muzzle into his palms. Ben would pull back. Finally one day, he reached out to pet her. When he stopped, she thrust her head at him again, but he turned away. A few days later, when Cassie approached him for another round of attention, Ben responded. About this time, Ben began to smile. Then, he began walking again, something the doctors had said would never happen. By the time he was able to sleep in a regular bed and sit comfortably in a chair, he had become the old Ben his family and friends had loved. He was a cheerful man who made it his responsibility to welcome visitors and newcomers to the community with Cassie by his side.

What was happening at Silverado got noticed. After Ben moved in, new residents began to arrive regularly. Lori, who was there from the beginning, wasn't surprised when a waiting list developed. "When people heard Loren speak about our vision – that we were there to provide the best memory care in the world – no one could doubt for a moment that what we were doing would succeed."

Chapter Ten

The Journey to Silverado

Sometimes you don't know when you're taking the first step through a door until you're already inside.

– Ann Voskamp

My name is Polly. About ten years ago, my mother started showing subtle changes in behavior. She became irritated easily and sometimes snapped at people, which was totally out of character. Then her memory began to fail. As her dementia progressed, I tried to help her remember plans, act appropriately, and dress well. Unfortunately, because my expectations of her were unreasonable, she perceived my constant reminders as criticism. She began to call me "the know-it-all," usually under her breath, but occasionally to my face. The hurt and misunderstanding that occurred between us before we realized what was going on was the most insidious aspect of her dementia.

I am telling my story in the hope that others might learn from my experience. That one of my parents would experience memory loss was the last thing on my mind. My parents were both independent, active people into their senior years. My father had been a pilot and entrepreneur. My mother attended nursing school. Later, she focused on giving her three children the best possible childhood, raising us to see the world as a place full of open arms and possibility. Having a love for world travel, our parents often took exciting trips with large groups of friends. My mother did all the research, mapping, and reservations for everybody.

When my father was diagnosed with cancer, things began to change. He survived, but it took a huge toll. Leaving their longtime home, my parents opted for a community that was easier to get around in. A year later, needing more assistance, they moved again. The following week, my father passed away. In the middle of our grief, my mother was told she could not continue to live there alone. We felt fortunate to locate an assisted living community close to my home where she had as much freedom as she wanted.

Eight months after moving in, she fell and broke her elbow. During an examination at the hospital, x-rays revealed that she also had an old hip fracture. So, the surgeon put a screw in her hip. Afterwards, he sent her to a rehabilitation facility, which he described as "a nice place to get her strength back." He gave instructions for "weight-bearing exercise as tolerated."

However, the doctor at the facility disagreed with the surgeon. The more my mother tried to get up and walk around, the more intent he was on stopping her. When my mother became upset, she struck out at one of the nurses. The staff's response was to put her in a plastic straitjacket and tell her she needed to calm down.

When I visited three days later, I found my mother heavily drugged and tied to a wheelchair next to the nurses' station. Urine was dripping from her seat onto the floor. I asked for a towel and directions to the shower. The staff said there was no need to wash her, because they showered the patients once a week.

"I'm doing it now," I told them, and I took her to the shower room. While I was showering her, she hit me. I wasn't angry; I understood her distress and rage. In an appointment with her surgeon a few days later, he discovered her arm had recently been re-broken. No one at the rehab facility had noticed. No wonder she wasn't happy.

Eventually, my mother moved back to her assisted living community. For a while, she was active again and able to walk from her apartment to the grocery store two blocks away.

Over time, however, her dementia became more evident. One day, the management contacted me to say she needed to move into their locked area immediately. While I tried to make the transition smooth for her, she was very distraught. She couldn't understand what she had done to cause this to happen. The staff gave her drugs to calm her down, which made her sleepy and affected her balance. Getting out of bed one morning, she hit her head on the dresser. After that, she was confined to a wheelchair because they said she was unstable. Shortly thereafter, she was sent to a psychiatric hospital to get her drugs "straightened out."

Within several days of arriving there, she was nearly comatose. When she wasn't in bed, they had her in a wheelchair with a "lap buddy" to keep her seated. I don't believe she was out of that chair much, if at all. Two weeks into her stay at the psychiatric hospital, she was completely unable to walk, her feet having swollen to the size of footballs. Short of "torture," there was no way to describe the way my mother was treated at both the rehab facility and the psychiatric hospital. In a matter of weeks, she went from a woman who loved walking to an incapacitated shell of a person. Finally, the psychiatric hospital sent her to a medical center, where doctors discovered that she had a severe urinary tract infection and that her whole body was in trouble.

Reeling from her stunning, rapid decline from too many drugs and inhumane care, I was desperate to find a place where I could be certain she would be treated like a human being. One evening when my husband and I were having dinner with friends, I poured out the whole story. Listening sympathetically, one of them referred me to his friend Donna who had worked for Silverado.

Donna was an angel. Through her, I connected with Silverado senior family ambassador Doreen, who listened closely and helped me find the solutions

I needed in order of importance. First thing, we placed my mother at Silverado.

When she arrived at Silverado, it was clear she was still severely overmedicated. As the drugs were reduced, my real mom began to emerge, smiling and aware of her surroundings. Although she was not yet capable of joining the engagement programs, we dared to have hope again.

What happened to us is typical of countless families faced with caring for parents, spouses, or others with dementia. We tend to assume that everyone in the elder care field knows more than we do. I learned that many of them do not.

Fortunately, my mother survived the nightmare and is thriving at Silverado. She has the support, encouragement, and love that she needs to be the best she can be at this phase of her life. She has both feet planted firmly in her world, and with that confidence, she can be happy and loving again. How I had missed my mother! Now I have her back.

One of nine children, Bobbie was a girl who grew up in an Air Force family that moved frequently around the globe. For fifteen years, Bobbie's grandmother, "Mama" accompanied the large family on their military postings, always relocating with them when new orders came. Although Bobbie easily made friends with local children everywhere they went, Bobbie especially enjoyed Mama's attention, taking walks and baking cookies with her.

At age ninety-nine, Mama returned to her beloved homeland of Guam, where she died in comfort surrounded by friends after a full satisfying life.

For Bobbie's parents, it was more complicated. Her mother was diagnosed with both Parkinson's and Alzheimer's in her late sixties. When it became too difficult to care for her at home, she was moved to an assisted living community that offered dementia care. Bobbie and the family visited her constantly. Bobbie's sister played the grand piano and led the residents in singing while their father popped corn for Bobbie to pass around.

Although their mother had wished to spend her final days at home, the family was unaware of home hospice for the terminally ill. She passed away at the assisted living community.

Two years later, Bobbie's father had a major heart attack. Gravely ill in the weeks that followed, he was placed on hospice. The loving kindness and attentiveness of the hospice staff touched Bobbie deeply. Watching them care for her father, she thought, "This is something I want to do."

After her father died, Bobbie contacted an assisted living community and offered to volunteer. Finding fulfillment, she expanded her efforts to other senior communities. She helped residents shop and escorted them to doctors' appointments. Noticing her talent and compassion, Silverado Hospice offered her a staff position overseeing its volunteers. Thus, Bobbie became a family care advocate and admissions coordinator.

In that capacity, Bobbie picked up the phone one day and heard distress on the other end of the line.

"My husband, Hal, was diagnosed with dementia three years ago," the voice said. "Am I speaking with someone who can help me?"

Bobbie assured her she was.

"My name is Phoebe. I've been taking care of Hal all this time, but I'm not sure how much longer I can hold up."

"We'll do everything we can," Bobbie said. "Tell me more about what's going on."

Her voice trembling, Phoebe explained that at first it had been manageable. Even though Hal's dementia worsened following his gall bladder surgery, she could still take him shopping and go to the park as long as she had help. What mattered was that they were together, partners in every sense of the word. Married over thirty years, they had worked together for two decades at Hal's business, and they were the parents of six children.

"Things are worse now," Phoebe went on. "He can't form sentences, brush his teeth, bathe, or handle toileting. And he doesn't always recognize me. I'm afraid his needs are overtaking my abilities."

Phoebe had spent many hours researching how to care for him and learning what he was going through. To her surprise, she discovered that hospice benefits are often available well before patients enter the process of actively dying. Searching the Internet, she found information about Silverado Hospice.

"That's how I found you," she told Bobbie over the phone. "I want the very best care for Hal, but I'm hoping he can remain at home with me." Her voice breaking, Phoebe added, "He's the love of my life."

"I understand completely," Bobbie said. "Let me tell you about what we do and how we might be able to assist you and Hal. We'll want to learn about Hal as a person, to understand his life story," she said. "We'd also like to get to know you and your family. That way, we can shape a care program that's just right for Hal and enable us to support and assist you as well."

Feeling the knot in her stomach start to ease, Phoebe asked, "What can I do to get started?"

"The first step is obtaining a physician's order for Hal to be evaluated and approved for hospice," Bobbie said. "If hospice care is deemed appropriate, he could be admitted. Now when I say 'admitted,' I mean enrolled in our hospice care program. He would continue to live with you at home, and we would come there to provide care."

"I'll contact our doctor right away," Phoebe said. When she hung up the phone, Phoebe got in her car and drove to the physician's office to ask for the order. Obtaining it, she called Bobbie back the same day.

"I have the physician's order from our doctor, and I'd like to come over with it right now," Phoebe told her. When she arrived at the Silverado Hospice office, a woman was waiting outside the building.

"Phoebe?" the woman asked.

"Yes," Phoebe responded.

"I'm Bobbie," the woman smiled, opening her arms wide. The two embraced, and tears filled Phoebe's eyes. She wasn't alone any more.

Bobbie escorted Phoebe into her office. After signing the consent form for Hal's hospice care to begin, Phoebe and Bobbie met with a Silverado colleague named Jennifer to discuss what would happen next. The team caring for Hal would include an attending physician, a medical director, a social worker, an R.N. case manager, aides, a spiritual care coordinator, as well as volunteers. Together they would care for Hal at home.

"Our focus is to make this time of Hal's life the best it can be," Jennifer said.

Bobbie leaned toward Phoebe and placed a lap blanket in her hands. "This is a gift from us to thank you for giving us the honor of caring for Hal," she said. "We are not only committed to being there for your husband; we are also there for you."

Touching the soft material, Phoebe felt hope and peace for the first time in years.

The next six months, the last of Hal's life, were as the couple wanted. They were together in their home because of Silverado Hospice. Phoebe knew her husband was in excellent hands with its care team. Just as important, Bobbie and the others with Silverado understood exactly what she was going through. They were always available to listen and offer encouragement. Their support enabled Phoebe to withstand the blow of Hal's death. Later, she would tell Bobbie that without her friendship and the help of Silverado Hospice, she might have turned to medicating her emotional pain. Instead, Phoebe was able to put one foot in front of the other and move forward.

Some months after Hal's passing, Phoebe and Bobbie met at a café. After they settled at their table, Phoebe reached into her handbag.

"Bobbie, since words will never express how much your support has meant to me, I am hoping this will show you how I feel," she said, giving Bobbie a small box.

Bobbie smiled. "I brought something for you, too," she said, pulling a package out of her tote bag.

"You don't need to give me a gift," Phoebe said. "You've done so much for me already."

"Phoebe, you've done just as much for me," Bobbie said. "Knowing that I've helped you tells me that I'm making a difference, that I'm achieving the purpose I had when I set out on this journey to assist others."

Both women were quiet for a moment. Then, they opened their presents. The box Phoebe gave Bobbie contained a crucifix, while Phoebe discovered a shadow box in the package from Bobbie.

"It's beautiful," they exclaimed in unison.

As much as they treasured those presents, Bobbie and Phoebe also shared the gift of an enduring friendship, which now touches many other people. These days, Phoebe volunteers alongside Bobbie as a family ambassador at Silverado Hospice. She donates many hours each month to helping others, recalling how she herself was once so much in need.

Milton's condition was progressing rapidly. He was forgetting things, suffering intense anxiety, slurring his words, and falling. Since the day he heard the doctor's diagnosis of Huntington's disease, he had gone from being a leader in a scientific field to a person who needed assistance with almost everything. The one constant in his life was his beloved dog Roscoe, who displayed endless loyalty and love for him.

However, a crisis was looming. Milton's condition was reaching a point where remaining at home would no longer be feasible. After his diagnosis, Milton had appointed his sister Elena to take charge of his affairs. Now, Elena was worried. What senior living community would allow Roscoe, an 85-pound Labrador retriever mix, to move in with her brother? Elena's initial round of calls confirmed her suspicions. The few that permitted dogs only accepted small ones. What's more, the dog's owner would be responsible for all of its needs, from walking and feeding to visits to the veterinarian. If the resident lost that capability, the dog would have to leave. Elena spent many anxious nights wondering what to do.

Then, a friend suggested Elena contact Silverado; he had heard it had a reputation for being pet-friendly. Skeptical as she was, she called Silverado. She was told, "It's true. We have a real menagerie here. Pets of all sizes are welcome." Instantly, Elena made an appointment to see for herself.

The German shepherd who greeted Elena at the door with tail wagging turned out to be just one of a variety of dogs, cats, birds, and fish living alongside Silverado residents. Silverado's family ambassador explained to her the presence of animals contributed to the community's overall living environment. Caring for the animals kept the residents connected to a purposeful life. For new residents especially, preserving the bond with their pet was vital.

"So often the memory impaired living at home lose connections with people," the family ambassador said. "As they become isolated, their dog or cat may be the one true friend that remains, always accepting them just as they are."

"You have described my brother's situation exactly," Elena said.

The family ambassador nodded. "That's why we encourage residents to bring their animals with them. As long as Roscoe gets along with the other pets, he is more than welcome here."

"What if my brother can't take care of Roscoe?" Elena asked.

"Believe me, that won't be a problem. Lots of people, including our other residents, will be happy to help."

When the day came for Milton to move to Silverado, Roscoe's dog bed was loaded into the truck along with his owner's furniture. For the next four years, the pair lived happily together at the community. Roscoe was almost always at Milton's side, except for periodic sojourns by the open door of the engagement director's office. He had taken a fancy to lying there on his stomach, chin on his paws, to watch the passing scene.

Those occasional times apart from his owner stopped when it became clear that Milton's life was ending. Staff members placed Roscoe's bowls next to Milton's bed, knowing that the dog would be unwilling to step away from his owner even for the short time it would take to eat and drink. As Milton drew his last breath, Roscoe's head lay on his hand.

Afterward, Roscoe retreated to quiet corners of Silverado, where he lay silent and motionless. His food went untouched.

"His heart is broken from losing Milton," Elena told Silverado's administrator, tears welling at the sound of her brother's name. "I don't know what to do, because I can't have Roscoe come to live with me."

"Silverado is Roscoe's home now," the administrator said. "We would be happy for him to stay here and be part of our family."

In relief, Elena hugged the other woman, saying, "Thank you so much. I know what this would have meant to my brother."

Everyone at Silverado did what they could to cheer up the sad dog. Residents and staff alike petted him, took him for walks, and invited him to sit with them. Family members brought treats to tempt his appetite. Finally one afternoon, the resident engagement director looked up from her desk with delight to find that Roscoe had returned to his post by her open door.

Chapter Eleven

Insist on Great Care

Love will find a way through paths where wolves fear to prey.

– Lord Byron

After nearly two decades of operating Silverado, Loren Shook has statistics that prove outstanding care can achieve landmark results: By the end of 2015, over 6,000 memory impaired people who couldn't walk when they arrived at Silverado had begun to walk again. More than 5,000 of those unable to eat on their own began feeding themselves.

"Silverado doesn't keep these records for bragging rights," Loren says. "From the beginning, our intention has been to raise the quality of care and quality of life for the memory impaired, not just at Silverado, but around the globe. We make our statistics public to give families a benchmark they can use to hold providers to a higher standard.

When Silverado's first senior living location was launched in Escondido, California, the staff maintained hand-written documentation on several topics such as ambulation, feeding, weight, hospitalizations, and falls. As Silverado grew into other areas, their tracked data widened as well. Now, computerized statistics provide real-time data on everything from pressure wounds to types and frequency of medication.

This measurable clinical data is not available anywhere else. Skilled nursing facilities are required to collect data on their patients. But assisted living organizations such as Silverado are not regulated the same way. However, Silverado voluntarily records their clinical data not only for its own use, but also for sharing it openly with other care providers. While Silverado encourages all providers to record and share the same data, the call has gone unheeded for the most part.

Loren maintains, "If all of us in the field of memory care came together to statistically record what works and what doesn't, we could collectively benefit millions of people everywhere. More families could demand better care for their loved ones rather than settle for the most acceptable local option."

Loren and Steve witness Silverado's impact every day. Having expanded greatly since its founding, Silverado now offers a continuum of care: Silverado At Home (home care and care management services), Silverado Communities, and Silverado Hospice. Loren and Steve visit all of Silverado's locations. It's not uncommon to see Loren chatting with a gentleman in the bistro of one of the communities or Steve walking arm-in-arm with a lady on a flowered path outside. They have never lost the exhilaration that comes from seeing a life changed for the better.

At the foundation of Silverado's practices is an emotion that is sorely lacking in healthcare today. That emotion is love. It's not just about feeling love; it's about expressing it. Loren's theme, *Love is greater than fear*, has always guided Silverado's operations. From this principle, nurses, caregivers, and other staff members base their actions on the best interests of those they serve, whether residents, patients, family members, or other employees. They are free to demonstrate love through words, actions, or hugs.

Unfortunately, in typical care centers or even in their own homes, those with deteriorating memory are bombarded each day with corrections, reminders, and rebukes.

"You already had breakfast."

"You've said the same thing five times today."

"You can't come with us. We won't be able to handle you."

This litany chips away at their self-esteem, blighting their spirits. Even as their cognitive function ebbs, they understand that they are now regarded as an embarrassment. As their physical and mental well-being declines, they find it's easier not to speak, not to participate. They would rather stay in bed than risk further rejection.

Silverado is committed to providing residents with an environment where they can succeed. They are not told they are wrong. They are in a place where the answer is "yes."

"Still hungry for more breakfast? Let's go find something you like."

"You always make me laugh with that story."

"The whole group is going; please come with us!"

"When a person comes into our care, the family usually gives us a list of all the things he or she can no longer do," related Anne Ellett, Silverado's former senior vice president of health services and a nurse practitioner with a master's degree in nursing. "They'll say 'She doesn't walk anymore; she doesn't feed herself; she doesn't want to participate in anything.' We thank them for the information, but we don't assume these limitations are permanent." At Silverado, a list of apparently lost abilities merely represents a description of how the memory impaired person seemed in a prior environment – at home or in another care community. Silverado conducts its own evaluation, keeping in mind that for the memory impaired, it's never one thing that makes a difference in their health; it's a combination of many things."

"A fresh assessment is a true advantage," according to Joe W. Ramsdell, M.D., Professor and Division Head, General Internal Medicine at the University of California, San Diego. "Behaviors which are developed in less supportive environments may not indicate how well a person will do at Silverado."

New residents are blank canvasses. With the first brushstroke, Silverado determines whether the new resident has received the right diagnosis. Although the general public uses the words "Alzheimer's" and "dementia" interchangeably, memory impairment can result from a range of causes. Symptoms may appear similar, but the progression of the conditions, the range of potential behavior, and the influence of assorted environments vary widely. Understanding the nature of the memory-impairing disease provides the platform on which to build an individual's care program.

More than half of the people who arrive at Silverado for care are taking too many medications, especially psychotropic drugs and sedatives which are often used to cope with so-called "behavior problems." Many are also taking medications that are no longer applicable to their health.

Often, a person previously prescribed blood pressure medication may be taking it long after his pressure has normalized. This may explain why he falls when he stands – his blood pressure is too low for him to sustain balance. Before he came to Silverado, caregivers probably solved the problem by tying him to his wheelchair, but continued to give him the blood pressure pills, which were the real culprits.

"A medication review can make a dramatic difference in the health and mobility of the memory impaired," agrees Dr. Ramsdell. By reducing the number and quantity of medications their residents take each day, Silverado's rate of fractures from falls drops below the national average.

Silverado assumes that everyone in its care is prone to falling. However, restraining them to wheelchairs and beds doesn't solve the problem or benefit overall health. Silverado never uses restraints of any kind, physical or pharmaceutical, believing such limitations deny the individual his or her rights. Human beings should have the opportunity to take risks. There is more dignity in risk than there is in being tied to a wheel chair.

Sometimes, family members resist Silverado's practice of liberating their loved one from restraints. The prospect of a fall naturally frightens them.

Invariably, they come to understand and celebrate the resident's restored dignity and the ability to be active and independent.

Silverado believes everyone can benefit from physical therapy. As a result, new residents are evaluated and placed on a physical therapy program as appropriate. After checking for factors that can affect gait and balance, such as proper shoes and glasses, Silverado encourages new residents who haven't been walking to try again. They may start by wearing a gait belt, which allows caregivers to walk beside them with a hand on the belt to provide assistance with balance. In addition, residents may wear hip protectors, padded garments designed to protect them in case of a fall.

Enjoyable activities are structured to encourage walking, for example group strolls or caring for Silverado's animals. Silverado combines walking and healthy nutrition by filling its country kitchens with finger foods, such as small sandwiches and pieces of fruit that hungry residents can snack on while taking a stroll. Since below-normal weight is common with the memory impaired, rebuilding weight and muscle is important in regaining the strength to walk.

Accompanying physical therapy, Silverado's restorative care program is the only one in the country designed specifically for the memory-impaired. The program seeks to reintroduce residents to activities of daily life. For instance, "hand-over-hand feeding" is used for residents who have not been able to handle their own fork and knife. At each meal, caregivers

> Hand-over-hand is a technique to help others learn or re-learn a lost activity or skill.

guide the resident's hand with their own. After a while, the resident relearns the skill of eating with utensils.

Silverado also assesses residents using a process called Behavior Mapping. During a resident's first three days at a community, caregivers record the resident's behavior every half-hour. What is she doing, what is she saying or not saying, what does she seem to like, when does she become hungry? Is she drawn to group activities or is she avoiding them? Nurses study the

Behavior Map to find patterns that will guide them in providing her with appropriate individual care.

Later, if the resident's behavior signals a departure from normal preferences and patterns, the staff uses the process again. The change may indicate an underlying problem that is not immediately obvious. For example, she may be in physical pain or emotional stress, but be unable to express herself through words. Behavior change is often an unspoken request for help. Analyzing the Behavior Map, the care team can usually identify the issue and resolve it.

According to Dr. Ramsdell, "A number of approaches that Silverado piloted have since been adopted by other care organizations, and the overall level of memory care in the country is starting to improve. Still, Silverado remains in a league of its own."

Susan Frazier is project guide for the Green House Project, a national nonprofit organization dedicated to creating meaningful long-term care environments. In her work, she consults with senior care communities nationwide. She remains inspired by a visit to Silverado that "rocked my world and opened my eyes to what could be done. I have been able to benefit residents, families, and staff with ideas I first saw at Silverado."

When Rose came to Silverado from a hospital at age 100, she was bedridden, unresponsive, suffering from pneumonia, and unable to eat without help. Rose had always been a strong, independent woman. Following her graduation from the University of Southern California, she raised her children and operated a pharmacy with her husband. For Rose's family, her physical incapacities were more distressing than her memory impairment.

Twenty-four hours after arriving at Silverado, Rose was able to rise from her bed and take part in a sing-along. Within weeks, she was walking the halls and handling her own fork, knife, and spoon in the dining room. Then, to everyone's surprise, she went on to win the baseball-throw competition at the local Senior Olympics.

"My mother participates in activities from eight in the morning until eight at night," her daughter, Dr. Janie Williams, declared. "She sings, she cooks, she participates in travel club, and she goes on outings. Once or twice, I have asked her if she would like to take a nap during the day, and she never wants to. She is living her life, loving her life."

Anyone who has experienced the anguish of a loved one's progressive memory impairment can understand how Rose's vibrancy has brought joy to her family.

"It's been wonderful," Dr. Williams affirmed. "Silverado enables us to enjoy doing things together again."

Rodney was a man of the cloth. For decades, he tenderly ministered to those in his flock during their most important moments. His grace and compassion made a wedding's joy even brighter and the sorrow of a memorial service more bearable. No one would have guessed this about Rodney seeing him the day he was rolled into Silverado on a gurney. He wore a hospital gown stained with food. A sticky dark substance smeared his face. Fearing it was blood, Silverado caregivers who gathered around him as he entered the front door discovered it was chocolate pudding, never wiped from his mouth and cheeks after an attempt to feed him.

Staff at the nursing home where he'd been living had tied down his hands and feet. "He lashes out physically and he yells all the time," they complained. Ultimately, they refused to care for him anymore.

Tamara, one of the Silverado staff greeting Rodney, took his hand and leaned down toward his ear. "Welcome," she whispered. "We love you. You are safe here. We are so glad you have come to live with us."

She and the other caregivers took Rodney to his room. When they lifted him from the gurney, they found he was lying on a plastic cup containing several pills. The medicine had clearly been meant for Rodney to take. No one at the nursing home noticed they were tying him down on top of it. The cup's rim had pushed a deep circular groove into his back. The bright red indentation had to be painful.

The caregivers rubbed a healing balm on Rodney's back. They cleaned him, dressed him in fresh and respectable clothes, and arranged his few things within his sight on his dresser. All the while, they continued to tell him he was loved, that he had come to a safe place.

Rodney was near the end of his time on earth. He no longer possessed the ability to speak. Those around him at Silverado remember him as an exceptionally peaceful man. He never raised a hand, never kicked, and never cried out. His expression was often contemplative, radiating a spirituality that made words unnecessary. Silverado gave Rodney what he had given so many others during his life. A warm welcome. Compassion. Safety. Love.

The house where Loren Shook's parents raised their children on the ground of Fairfax Hospital in Kirkland, Washington

Loren's aunt and uncle Marion and Bernard Hambleton

Kathleen Shook, Loren's mother, in the kitchen of Fairfax Hospital

Loren's aunt, Marion Hambleton, at work in the Fairfax Hospital admissions office

Loren atop Mt. Rainier

Loren Shook as a young boy

Main house at Glacier View Ranch in Northern Washington, where Loren worked during summer as a young man

Heidi the Palomino with friend, Kathy, on the Fairfax Hospital grounds

Seattle newspaper clipping announcing the opening of Fairfax Hospital's "new" treatment center

ARCHITECT'S DRAWING OF NEW PSYCHIATRIC TREATMENT CENTER IN JUANITA
Original Hospital Was Floated and Towed Across Lake From Seattle

Fairfax Psychiatric Hospital opens

Fairfax Psychiatric Hospital at 10218 N. E. 132nd St. is a blending of old and new.

The new is a modern psychiatric treatment center that was opened Sunday for public viewing. The old is the original Fairfax Hospital building on Queen Anne Hill that was "floated and towed" across Lake Washington in 1934.

The hospital was founded in 1929 and was incorporated in 1957. Mr. and Mrs. Bernard Hambleton, owners, have operated the hospital since 1950.

* * *

LOCATED in a countrylike atmosphere, the hospital is on approximately 30 acres where some patients are able to ride horseback. The new facility is one-story with both open and closed door accommodations. Included is a large lounge and

recreational area and occupational therapy space with a full-time therapist.

Bed capacity at the present time is 80 beds with space to expand to 99 as needed. Both male and female patients are admitted with no age limit. Admissions may be voluntary or by commitment. All patients are under the care of a physician or psychiatrist.

The older portion of the hospital is planned to be used as a geriatric center for care of the aged. It will have a 32 bed capacity.

Frederick Lemere, M.D., is medical director of the hospital.

Hambleton, administrator, is a member of the American College of Hospital Administrators. He has had four years experience as assistant admin-

istrator and 17 years as administrator.

Marian Hambleton, R. N., is director of nursing. She received her bachelor of science degree in nursing from the University of Washington and has had eight years experience as a staff nurse and 13 years experience as director of nursing.

The medical staff consists of 36 physicians, including psychiatrists, general practitioners, internists. The staff is organized in accordance with standards of the Joint Commission on Accreditation of Hospitals.

* * *

Personnel includes a nursing staff of 25, including registered nurses, practical nurses and nurses aids. Total personnel is 42.

The hospital is licensed by the State Department of Health of Washington, approved by Medicare and is a member of the American Hospital Association, Washington State Hospital Association and the National Association of Private Psychiatric Hospitals.

Types of care given include psychotherapy, psychoanalysis, electroshock therapy, sub-

coma-insula therapy, occupational therapy and recreational therapy.

* * *

TYPES OF patients include extreme senility, acute treatment, outpatients, night care, custodial care, rehabilitation, day care, dope addiction "drying out", LSD patients, alcoholics, and in-patient.

The new Fairfax Psychiatric Hospital was designed and built through the efforts of Mr. and Mrs. Hambleton, Willis McClarty, architect; Gene E. Lyon consultant and builder, and William R. Hanson, construction engineer.

Others contributing were Harry Broman and Ira Cummins, architects for Washington State Health Department; Miss Helen Levitt, Washington State Nursing Consultant to Psychiatric Care Facilities; Mr. Besse, Washington State Sanitarium; Clarence Ross, assistant Washington State Fire Marshal; Dr. A. B. Price, head of the planning and construction section of the Washington State Department of Health.

Construction was by Careage Construction Corp. at a cost of $750,000.

Fairfax Hospital Recreation building

Steve as an infant with his mother, Frances and sister Cheri

Steve skiing in Lake Tahoe

Steve Winner at a group home in Chesterfield County, VA

Steve and Deanelle Winner

Steve sits with a family member and resident at Silverado Escondido, where he served as an administrator in the company's early days

Steve with his daughter, Elizabeth and grandson, Ian

Silverado Founders
The late Jim Smith, Steve Winner and Loren Shook

Rose Arrington appears on Times Square Jumbotron

Residents and an associate petting the miniature horses at Silverado Encinitas

2000's

Suzanne & Loren Shook

Cameron Pereyra

Loren and his son Aaron

so they'll have enough!

Left to Right – Aaron Shook, Heather Shook-Pereyra, Linden Pereyra, James Pereyra, Suzanne Shook, Loren Shook, Christine ("Chrissy") Shook

Loren & Christine ("Chrissy")

Left to Right – Christine ("Chrissy"), Loren, Arianna Shook, Heather Shook-Pereyra

Left to Right – John-Colby Shook, Loren Shook, Suzanne Shook, Arianna Shook

Clockwise – Heather Shook-Pereyra, Suzanne Shook & Linden Pereyra

The Silverado Difference

Your purpose is your why.

– Deborah Day

Kathy had worked at a nursing home where dementia patients spent their day strapped into wheelchairs. Sedatives dulled their ability and their inclination to do much more. When she visited Silverado for an employment interview, what she saw frightened her.

"Residents were walking about freely. I had never seen such a thing. I thought it was dangerous."

Startled as she was, she accepted the position as a resident engagement assistant. Helping with Silverado's Culinary Club on her first day, she gasped when the residents picked up knives and started slicing potatoes. Working at Silverado was going to be different.

Like Kathy, many first-time visitors to Silverado are taken aback when they see residents performing normal tasks. At other long-term care programs, those with dementia are commonly provided with very easy activities and pastimes, usually under the direction of a single staff member with little training. It is generally assumed that the memory impaired are only capable of the simplest tasks.

Disproving that assumption has been a primary focus at Silverado since its founding. The organization's insistence on purposeful activities is central to overall care and it is the key to restoring purpose and well-being. The way residents spend their time affects them profoundly. When they take part in childish or inappropriate pastimes, it diminishes their self-esteem and eliminates the status that comes with defined roles and purpose.

Few things spark the ire of Loren Shook and Steve Winner faster than the sight of memory-impaired people wielding crayons over coloring books or gluing Popsicle sticks together. Yet, these activities too often make up the backbone of Alzheimer's care programs. People with dementia might have significant needs, but they are not children. They are capable of making decisions and choices. The memory impaired have the right and the need to do tasks that illustrate their competence and value, things that anyone else their age might do.

Kathy, now her community's resident engagement director, moved confidently through the dining room of her Silverado community. As lunch was finishing up, she greeted residents along the way.

"Hi, Ron, how are you doing?"

Ron shoved his chair back from the table, stood, and strode past Kathy without a word. Stopping at the dining room's open door, he turned back to face Kathy with a scowl while grasping both sides of the doorframe so tightly his knuckles went white.

Ron had come to Silverado from a geriatric hospital near his lifelong home a thousand miles away. Its staff had told Ron's family that his outbursts were so frequent and frightening that he needed to be placed in a psychiatric facility, the sooner the better.

Fortunately, Ron's daughter lived near this Silverado community, and she had heard good things about it. Maybe something could be done for Dad, she told her family. So Ron had arrived three weeks earlier.

In that short time, Silverado staff discovered that going out to the garden calmed Ron's anger. It made sense. From interviews with his family, they learned he had lived on a farm when he was younger. Staff members encouraged Ron to talk about those days, and sometimes he did.

From her training and experience at Silverado, Kathy was certain Ron's anger was not a symptom of his dementia. Behavior is never a symptom. It is an expression of needs, psychological or physical, that the memory impaired can no longer communicate or act upon in a manner considered normal. For a man accustomed to vigorous activity performed in the fresh air, being confined to the geriatric hospital must have been torturous. No wonder he had expressed such rage there, Kathy thought. He had been denied the life that mattered to him.

Several days after Ron had discovered the garden, Kathy was in an informal meeting in Silverado's living room. Sitting in a circle made of chairs and a sofa were Silverado members of the R.F.A., the community's Retired Farmers of America Club. The club concept is a fundamental Silverado principle meant to engage residents in meaningful programs. Kathy suggested something that had been on her mind for a while. "We should ask Ron to help us build a chicken coop," she said. The members nodded in agreement.

When people with memory impairment are asked if they want to go to an activity, they often don't understand what is being requested of them. Uncertainty usually leads them to say no. Reminding them to attend club meetings is a different matter. Silverado's residents are mostly of the generation that commonly participated in card clubs, veteran's clubs, women's clubs, or men's clubs. Along these lines, Silverado assesses the particular interests of its current residents and designs clubs to match them. Cooking "activities" become the Culinary Club. Exercise programs turn into the Fitness Club. Garden activities form the Garden Club.

Membership in a club not only conveys belonging and exclusivity, but also builds self-esteem. It also leads to far more participation. So, rather than ask a resident whether she wishes to attend an activity, staff members say,

"Your club is meeting. You are a member and you're needed. I'll take you."

At Kathy's community, a number of former farmers had been living there even before Ron's arrival, inspiring the establishment of the Retired Farmers of America Club. Now, with its members giving their blessing to the chicken coop project, Kathy researched local ordinances and gathered possible designs. She also got in touch with a Boy Scout who had called offering his services as a volunteer.

The day of the next club meeting, she approached Ron. Sitting by himself in the living room, he appeared stiff, his face frozen.

"The Retired Farmers of America Club would like to build a chicken coop, and we need your help," Kathy said. "I'm headed over there now – we can go together."

Ron looked at Kathy. He didn't say anything.

"There's a Boy Scout, Josh, who wants to work on the chicken coop, too," Kathy said. "Building the coop would help Josh make Eagle Scout. He isn't exactly sure how to do it, and he is hoping you can advise him, since you have more experience. He really can't do it without you. Please come."

There was a moment more of silence. Then Ron stood up. "Okay," he said. Kathy linked her arm with his, and they made their way to the club meeting. Josh, the Boy Scout, was there along with the members, and the group was already gathered around a table looking through a book on chicken coop layouts. Ron took an empty seat between two club members. Turning to a page showing two designs, Kathy slid the book toward him and asked which he recommended. It took him only a few moments to point and say, "This, definitely this."

Ron and Josh spent the succeeding days in Silverado's backyard, the coop gradually taking shape from their efforts. Other members of the club offered advice and encouragement. As hoped, Ron's expressions of anger began to diminish. When three Rhode Island Reds moved into the structure, feeding, watering, and collecting eggs became a morning routine for Ron. His outbursts disappeared entirely.

Now, several years after Ron's passing, he is remembered as the calm man whose handiwork established a much-loved tradition. Every morning at his Silverado community, residents still enjoy going out to the coop to gather eggs.

In many memory care programs, giving residents baby dolls to hold, diaper, and feed is a standard practice, a well-meaning effort to fulfill the human need to nurture. Silverado, however, prohibits these practices because they are not age-appropriate. Instead, Silverado offers a different avenue for residents to experience the reward of nurturing, which explains what Cheryl, a Silverado resident engagement assistant, did one day. Hearing rapid footsteps behind her in the hallway, Cheryl knew who it was even before she saw her.

"Alvina, good morning," she said, turning and smiling at the woman approaching her. Alvina walked by without answering. As usual, she was wringing her hands. Ever since Alvina had moved into Silverado two weeks earlier, the staff had been working to understand to calm the anxiety that kept the resident pacing much of the day and sometimes into the night.

"Alvina, I'm glad I happened to see you, because we need your help with something," she said, hurrying to catch up with her. Falling into step with Alvina, she continued. "We have a new resident and we need someone special to help introduce her to her home here. You are the absolute perfect person to do this. Could you please help?" Alvina gave a sidelong glance at Cheryl. Encouraged, Cheryl added, "I know you're the only person who can do this."

There was a moment of silence. Then Alvina nodded and said, "All right."

"Her name is Dolly, and she is in the administrator's office right now," Cheryl said. "Let's go, and I'll introduce you."

The office door was normally kept open. Every area at Silverado is considered part of the residents' home; they have the right to come and go as they wish. Today, it was closed. Without hesitation, Cheryl turned the knob and gestured for Alvina to step inside with her. A black Labrador retriever sprang up from the cushion where it had been lying.

"Alvina, this is Dolly," Cheryl said. "We just adopted her from the shelter, so she isn't accustomed to being here yet. Can you help her explore the community and get used to things?"

Alvina unclenched her hands. Letting Dolly sniff her hand, Alvina was cradling Dolly's head within seconds. She bent down and whispered, "You are beautiful." For the first time since she had arrived at Silverado, Alvina looked relaxed.

From that moment, the two were inseparable. Alvina spent happy days walking Dolly, feeding her, and throwing sticks and balls for her in the backyard. With the Labrador retriever flourishing under her care, Alvina no longer paced or wrung her hands. Her need to nurture a life was fulfilled and her love for the animal was reciprocated.

Caring for pets rather than baby dolls provides a normal, age-appropriate way for the memory impaired to nurture. Recognizing the clear benefits to both residents and pets is the reason Silverado adopts so many dogs, cats, and other animals from shelters and rescue organizations. Silverado also strongly encourages residents to move in with their own pets. And, unlike other senior living organizations that accept pets, if a resident becomes unable to take care of his or her animal, Silverado will continue indefinitely to house and care for it or find it a good home.

One of Silverado's guiding philosophies is that all interactions a resident has with other residents or staff should have meaning. Therefore, it has discarded the word "activities," as in "Activities Program," in favor of "engagement" or "club."

"Engagement is something that happens continually," explains Alisa, a

Silverado resident engagement director. "It's not simply a matter of putting events on a calendar, like 'Music at 2:00 p.m.' Instead, we look at engaging with the residents as a process that happens from the moment we arrive in the morning."

That's why whenever Alisa runs into Jill, a resident whose passion for dance leads her to wear tap shoes all day long, the two women break into an impromptu routine, sometimes in the middle of the dining room during lunch.

Another example comes from resident engagement director Gloria. Jack, a non-communicative resident, always avoided taking part in Silverado's clubs and events. Knowing Jack had designed a car engine during his career, Gloria borrowed a coffee-table book on automobiles from a friend and brought it to Silverado. She invited Jack to sit with her to look through its pages. It developed into a morning routine for the pair.

Then one Sunday morning, during a worship service at the community, Gloria sensed a presence at her side. She turned and found Jack standing beside her. It was the first time he had ever come to the gathering. When the next hymn began and Gloria started to sing, Jack's voice joined hers. "I couldn't believe it," Gloria says. "I started choking up. When the service was over, I thanked Jack for coming and told him how much it meant to me."

Jack passed away the next morning. "I know that before he left us, Jack had become free to express himself again," Gloria reminisces, still awed that sharing a book about cars had sparked Jack's re-engagement in life.

Understanding residents' interests and abilities is crucial to successful engagement. When new residents come to Silverado, engagement directors interview the residents themselves and their families to learn about their careers and hobbies, both current and past. In addition, the director of health services assesses their physical and cognitive capabilities. The insights gathered guide the staff in designing meaningful programs. Unfortunately, other long-term care communities typically fail to conduct such extensive evaluations. Residents are simply grouped into whatever activities are available with no consideration of appropriateness. Thus, when large groups of residents gather for a program, only two or three are responsive, while the rest are disengaged or sleeping. Clearly such activities are either too difficult or too easy for the functional abilities of the participants. The residents are bored and even humiliated.

Matching residents' capabilities and keeping pace with how they change over time is essential. This is why within each Silverado community there are three "neighborhoods" where residents live and interact with others whose abilities parallel their own. The Nexus Neighborhood is designed for people in the early stages of memory impairment. The Supportive Neighborhood serves those in the middle phase. The Sensory Neighborhood cares for residents in the later stages.

The neighborhoods' engagement programs are similar, but the approach is different for each group. An example is the Culinary Club, popular throughout Silverado. In the Nexus Neighborhood, club members take active roles in discussing menus and preparing the food. In fact, they shop for the ingredients.

Culinary Club participants in the Supportive Neighborhood may be asked to choose between two menus. At the supermarket, engagement staff may ask them to help decide which of two tomatoes looks riper. When the time comes for the residents to slice the tomatoes, a staff member helps them get started on the task.

In the Sensory Neighborhood, programs focus on triggering memories by unlocking the senses. For instance, a staff member may give Culinary Club participants tomatoes and carrots to hold as a way to feel shapes and textures. Staff may also let the residents dip their hands into a warm sauce to enjoy its temperature and consistency. Additionally, the scent of the food provides familiar pleasures and may stir up recollections associated with the aroma.

Whether residents in the three Neighborhoods remember what they did in Culinary Club is not the point, however. What matters is that positive feelings generated by the engagement remain. Silverado calls this concept the "self-esteem bank." By treating the memory impaired with respect and dignity and by providing multiple sensory opportunities, Silverado builds their self-worth. It sustains them and wards off depression; in the long run, they are happier and more satisfied.

Choice is often denied to those with dementia. Whether at home or in traditional memory care settings, others usually decide what time they get up, what they wear, eat, and drink, how they spend the day, and when they go back to bed. At Silverado, choice is at the center of its engagement programs. If residents decide to form a bowling club, members will choose their own balls, gloves, and club shirts, which will be specially designed based on member input. Positive reinforcement accompanies choices: "Great job picking that ball; it looks good with your shirt." Compliments make everyone feel good, even people with dementia.

Sandra sighed heavily and slumped her shoulders. Turning her face downward, she looked at her hands clasped in her lap.

"You're sad," said a man in the group sitting in a semi-circle facing Sandra's chair. She shook her head.

"Tired," another man said. "You're tired." His comment brought another head shake. "I know," a woman said. "You feel lonely."

"Yes," said Sandra. "That's it. I feel lonely."

The other members in Silverado's Drama Club applauded as Sandra moved back to her seat among them. Then, attention shifted to Alfred, who took his place where Sandra had been. It was his turn to portray the emotion suggested to him by the resident engagement assistant who was sitting amid the club members.

Silverado's Drama Club is a good example of the emphasis on interactivity.

In a typical long-term care activity program elsewhere, the activity director stands in front of the group or sits at the head of a table to present information. That approach discourages interaction. Silverado's staff, on the other hand, is trained to encourage residents to share their ideas, memories, and feelings. This free expression raises confidence and self-worth; it connects the memory impaired to the world around them. It also promotes their communication skills, sustaining them as long as possible during the progression of the disease.

Melinda stood against the bedroom wall, holding one end of the measuring tape as her husband, Jason, walked across the room.

"Can we make it work?" she asked.

"I think so," Jason responded pensively. "We aren't going to be able to fit everything your dad has, of course, but we should be able to bring the furniture that matters the most to him. I think we can arrange things so it looks similar to where he is now. "

"Thank goodness," Melinda said with relief. If anyone could set this Silverado room up so that it was right for her father, it was Jason. He was an architect. With Melinda's help, he had spent much of the afternoon measuring the space and making detailed notes. Her dad, Ken, could no longer stay at the independent living community across town. For several years, Ken had resided there with his wife, Mary, and their dog, Webster. When Mary passed away, he no longer had her loving help in coping with his progressing dementia. The absence of the woman he adored left a painful void in his life. As a result, Ken had begun to display a quick, uncharacteristic anger. At night, he roamed away from his apartment building. Webster trotted on a leash beside him, loyal to his master, but unable to turn him back toward home.

Melinda and Jason knew little about memory care communities, but family friends had suggested Silverado could be the right place for Ken. When the couple visited, Silverado residents and staff members were welcoming.

The lively atmosphere was a striking difference from other places they had visited. That Webster was invited to move in with Ken was a happy relief, but his room at Silverado would be smaller than the spacious two-bedroom apartment he was leaving. What about all the furnishings that Ken, an accomplished woodworker, had made in his younger years?

"It will be fine," the staff assured the couple. "We're sure there's enough space for the most important pieces. At any rate, with all the things to do here, he won't spend much time in his room. His home is the entire community. His room is just where he sleeps and takes care of his personal needs."

Despite this optimism, Melinda and Jason had more than one sleepless night in the days leading up to Ken's move to Silverado. They worried about how Ken would adjust to the downsized room, and they felt guilty, wondering if they were shortchanging him with the smaller space. Melinda's stomach was in knots as they drove to pick up Ken on the day of the move. At a red light, Jason reached over and squeezed her hand. "We'll see how he adjusts to the room," he said. "If it's too small or he's unhappy at Silverado, we'll figure out something else."

When Melinda, Jason, Ken, and Webster arrived at Silverado, a man and two women met them at the front door.

"Hi, I'm Joseph," the man said, smiling and extending his arm for a handshake with Ken. "I live here."

The two women, both members of Silverado's staff, told them Ken's room was ready. Working from the floor plan that Jason had provided, they and some others had arrived early that morning to move in Ken's furniture, artwork, and other belongings.

"Everything fit perfectly," they said. "We think you're going to love it."

The women stooped to pet Webster and, with Ken's permission, gave him a treat. Then Joseph said, "Come along, and we'll take you to your room."

Walking down the hallway, they heard the sound of hammering. As they approached an open door, Ken paused and looked inside. Five men and a woman were driving nails into pieces of wood. It looked like they were building a pair of small tables.

"Hmm," Ken said.

When the group got to Ken's room, Melinda felt her pulse accelerate. She could see from the threshold that the Silverado staff had followed Jason's floor plan to the letter. But what would her father think?

Ken and Webster stepped inside. He looked around for a few moments and dropped Webster's leash so he could explore and sniff.

After a few moments, Ken said, "This is great." He sat down in the armchair he had built in his basement woodshop when Melinda was a teenager. He said again, "This is great."

When Melinda and Jason left Silverado that day, they decided to give Ken some time to settle in before going back to see him. If there were problems, they knew Silverado would call. The phone remained silent. Three days after Ken moved in, the couple came to visit him. When they arrived at his room, Ken wasn't there and neither was Webster. Alarmed, they went back to the front lobby to ask if anyone knew where they were.

"Oh, Ken's at Woodworking Club, and Webster is probably with him," said a caregiver who was sitting and chatting with several residents. She pointed down the hallway, in the direction of the room where people had been hammering the day of Ken's arrival. Melinda and Jason hurried there. From the doorway, they saw the same people who had been there previously. This time, they were measuring pieces of wood. Ken was with them, a tape measure in his hand. Webster was sleeping under his chair. Ken, sensing a presence, looked up toward the door and nodded at them. Then, he went back to what he was doing.

Melinda and Jason quickly learned not to visit during Woodworking Club;

Ken was too busy to talk to them. They also stopped going right to Ken's room when they arrived at Silverado. If Ken wasn't involved in woodworking, he might be playing pool, putting on the green out back, or watching a basketball game with the Men's Club, Webster always his constant companion. The anger he had expressed before was never shown at Silverado, and he made no effort to roam from the community.

One day, when Melinda caught Ken between activities and was talking with him, her father suddenly turned and strode away from her. For a moment, she felt hurt. "Then I realized that my father felt that the entire Silverado community was his home. His walking away from me showed that he was at ease here, that it was like he was going from one room to another in his own house."

Stopping in at a Silverado community one Saturday, Loren and Steve found residents in the backyard shooting arrows at targets; the Archery Club was having a competition. The sight would have astonished many, but Loren and Steve were delighted by the innovation. Silverado constantly evolves its engagement program in response to the latest findings on dementia. When research showed that exercise improves cognition, archery was among the newest fitness programs Silverado launched. More art, storytelling, and music have been incorporated too, because findings indicate that using the creative portion of the brain may boost communication skills.

Engagement program innovation is so important that it is part of the demanding normalization audit made by visiting teams of Silverado employees. On its one-to-five scale, a three is given for being free of age-inappropriate activities. Attaining the higher marks of four or five requires that engagement programs not only be groundbreaking and compelling, but also promote confidence and choice. Every year, more Silverado communities are attaining the better rankings as the residents and staff members push the boundaries of what the memory-impaired can do.

Some years ago, when the nation's new president took the helm, he looked out across the sea of faces and called for a fresh era of responsibility in

America. A television screen and three thousand miles separated him from the twelve memory-impaired people seated in a semicircle in the Silverado community in Costa Mesa, California. But he seemed to speak directly to them, for each one had always had a purpose in life. Some served in wartime. Others assisted the effort on the home front. They raised their kids and held down jobs; they volunteered in schools, churches, food pantries, and hospitals. When they retired, they looked forward to having more time to contribute to their communities.

Lives don't always go according to plan, however, and faltering memories brought the twelve individuals to Silverado. Here, they helped care for children, tended gardens, worked with animals, painted artwork, and built useful things. After the president's address, they pulled their chairs closer together in Silverado's living room and began talking about how they yearned to contribute further. They wanted to volunteer outside Silverado's doors. They were going to show everyone what the memory impaired can do.

The Silverado Service Club was born. Its steering committee meets biweekly to discuss volunteer work in progress and to make new plans. Its initial project had residents knitting blankets and delivering them to newborns in a local hospital. Residents at other Silverado communities quickly became inspired to form their own service clubs. Now, on any given day throughout the cities and towns that Silverado serves, those with dementia are fanning out into the greater community to make life better for people without memory impairment.

Lives with meaning empowered by a purpose-driven organization: That was what Loren Shook and Steve Winner and their colleague, the late Jim Smith, envisioned when they established Silverado. Thousands of memory-impaired people at Silverado have begun to walk and feed themselves again, but Silverado engagement programs have provided them the reason to do so. They walk because they have something to walk to. They nourish their bodies to participate in life, or as Silverado puts it, L.I.F.E: Love, Innovation, Family, and Engagement.

Loren and Steve are admiring spectators of the Silverado Service Club. The residents receive assistance from staff at their community, but the vision and desire to contribute to the world is theirs. Rekindle the inner spirit and it can burn brighter and stronger than even Loren, Steve, or Jim ever thought possible.

Chapter Thirteen

Compassionate Caregivers

I believe that every single event in life happens in an opportunity to choose love over fear.

– Oprah Winfrey

Esmeralda's parents were California farm workers. Alternating their work schedules, one worked in the fields while the other was at home with Esmeralda and her three siblings. The children dreaded the days their father stayed with them. When his alcoholism unexpectedly boiled over into a rage, the youngsters could do nothing but cower from the blows.

When she was eight, Esmeralda befriended a woman named Beatrice who lived in a senior complex next to her family's house. Daily, the two met outside for a friendly chat. Sometimes Beatrice asked Esmeralda to do little errands for her and the little girl was always happy to comply.

On a day when her daughter was due to visit, Beatrice asked the child to hide her cigarettes, offering her jewelry in exchange for the favor. Later, Esmeralda took the jewelry to the manager of the senior complex to give back to Beatrice.

When Beatrice's daughter learned Esmeralda had returned the jewelry, she asked the little girl, "How old are you? How did you know to give it back?" And she tried to give her five dollars for her honesty, but Esmeralda refused; it had never occurred to her to keep the jewelry.

One day, Beatrice failed to appear. She wasn't there the next day or all the rest of the week. When Esmeralda found out the elderly woman had passed away, she grieved her friend's absence, missing their non-threatening relationship.

The refuge for Esmeralda and her siblings became a man named Juan and his wife, who lived down the street from Esmeralda's family. She and her siblings treasured Juan's calm, steady presence. One day when Esmeralda was a young teenager, she was at Juan's home when he doubled up with excruciating pain. He was taken to a hospital and passed away a month later.

When Esmeralda and her siblings learned of his death, they were inconsolable. Juan had been their only protection against their alcoholic father. He was the person they had turned to for kindness and compassion. As the four of them walked in the direction of their friend's house, they were red-eyed and crying.

"Why is God punishing us?" her bother sobbed.

Esmeralda answered, "God's not punishing us. We all have to go through some kind of pain and suffering." The four children walked together in silence.

Now a Silverado caregiver, Esmeralda paused at the threshold of an open door and tapped gently on its frame. The white-haired couple inside looked up at her and the man motioned for Esmeralda to come in.

"We're just getting Winnie's knick-knacks arranged on the dresser, and then she'll be all set," he said as Esmeralda entered.

Esmeralda nodded and turned toward Winnie. "It's so nice to meet you," she said. "I am going to be your caregiver. Is that all right with you?"

"I don't have a choice," Winnie said, pursing her lips and folding her arms tightly across her chest.

Winnie's husband, Steve, flinched at the response and opened his mouth to offer an apology. Esmeralda smiled at him to show it wasn't necessary. From interviews Silverado had conducted with Winnie and her family, Esmeralda knew Winnie had a strong personality. Her two children said their mom never let them get away with anything when they were growing up. After Winnie was diagnosed with Alzheimer's, she continued living at home with Steve, even working as the administrative assistant in his business. Getting a job done and done right was important to her; any difficulties were to be navigated no matter the effort.

Because her condition had progressed, she had moved to Silverado. Steve assured everyone at Silverado that he was happy to have found such a vibrant place, but Winnie was devastated to have left the home and the life she had known. Her repeated phrase, "I don't have a choice," was her way of expressing the pain of feeling powerless. As Winnie's caregiver, Esmeralda would not only assist Winnie with her physical needs; she would also try to connect with her and give her back her sense of self-determination.

The opportunity to have this kind of impact was what had brought Esmeralda to Silverado. After growing up, she had become a stay-at-home mother of three with no plans to pursue a career outside the home. But her friend Guillermina had joined Silverado as a caregiver, and when she talked about her work, it became clear that she did more than assist the memory impaired with their personal needs. She knew them as individuals and did what she could to help them find happiness and purpose despite their condition.

Inspired by her friend, Esmeralda inquired about a position at Silverado. Her compassionate nature was so evident that she was quickly hired. At the time Winnie moved in, Esmeralda had been a caregiver at Silverado for six years.

"No, no, no!" Winnie exclaimed, pushing Esmeralda's hands away. "Leave it alone. Leave me alone!"

"Of course, I will leave you alone if that is what you want," Esmeralda said. Ever since Winnie had moved in the previous week, she had been resisting her assistance. "But your bracelet is so pretty. I thought you might like me to take it off and put it on your dresser. That way you can put it right back on when you go out tomorrow."

Saying nothing for a moment, Winnie knotted her hands, unknotted them, and knotted them again. Then, studying Esmeralda's face, she said, "Tomorrow, there's something I'd like to do."

"What is it?" Esmeralda asked.

"I'd like to start planning a shelter," Winnie replied.

"How wonderful," Esmeralda said. "What kind of shelter?"

"For women whose husbands are abusing them."

"You'd like to create a safe place for them. That's so thoughtful of you," Esmeralda said.

"No, not just a safe place," Winnie went on. "We'll give classes. The women can learn new things and find jobs."

"Oh, I understand. So they wouldn't have to be dependent on the men who abused them. They could take control of their lives. They wouldn't be powerless anymore."

As Winnie nodded, Esmeralda stood still for a moment, gazing at her. With her comments, Winnie had just opened the first crack in her combative exterior to reveal who she really was. Winnie felt compassion for those who did not have a loving spouse like her Stevie, who visited her like clockwork every day, always wrapping his arms around her and calling her "my bestest friend." After a few moments, Esmeralda reached gently toward Winnie, who held out her arm. She unclasped Winnie's bracelet and laid it on top of her dresser.

Entering Winnie's room one day, Esmeralda had tears in her eyes. Her young son had Kawasaki disease, a rare childhood illness that causes blood vessel inflammation and sometimes affects coronary arteries. The doctor said the prognosis was good, but Esmeralda was worried. Sensing her anxiety, Winnie looked at her questioningly.

"My little boy is ill," Esmeralda told her.

Winnie nodded her understanding and began saying the Hail Mary Prayer. When she finished, she gazed at Esmeralda and said, "It will be all right."

Her words brought a deep feeling of peace to Esmeralda and her son recovered three weeks later.

As Winnie's health began to decline, her ability to speak dwindled, but the connection between the two women remained strong. Esmeralda shampooed Winnie's hair and rubbed her hands with her favorite scented lotions. When doctors determined Winnie's life was nearing an end, Esmeralda was certain she still appreciated her attention and knowing this gave Esmeralda pleasure.

During lunch in Silverado's dining room one afternoon, Esmeralda suddenly had the feeling that God wanted her to go to Winnie. As she hurried toward her room, a nurse saw her and said, "Esmeralda, you need to see Winnie right now." Arriving, she found Steve and their daughter by Winnie's bed and she joined them. Winnie tried to say something, but it wasn't clear what she meant. Then she became silent as life left her body.

Esmeralda remained at Winnie's side for a few minutes, until she felt ready to take leave of the woman who had meant so much to her. She kissed Winnie and hugged the others. Tears streamed down her face as she made her way back to the dining room, more by instinct than thought. When she entered, she spotted Doreen, a Silverado senior family ambassador, sitting at a table and she went to her.

"Doreen, my Winnie is gone," Esmeralda said, her voice breaking.

"Oh, Esmeralda, I am so sorry," said Doreen, rising to hug her. "I know how much you and Winnie loved each other."

"She wasn't well, and she is in a better place now, but I am going to miss her so much," Esmeralda said, accepting tissues from Doreen and wiping her eyes.

"I know," Doreen said. "We all will. She was a special lady. But just remember that her life was richer for knowing you, Esmeralda."

"Thank you," Esmeralda said. The two women talked for a few more moments. Then Esmeralda left the dining room for the garden to remember her friend.

Meanwhile, Doreen turned back to the couple having lunch with her. Melanie had recently moved into Silverado. Though she was doing well, her husband Joel was still not certain coming here was the right decision.

"Everything seems fine so far," Joel had told Doreen when she called to touch base with him a few days earlier. "But I still don't have a sense of peace about this." To discuss the matter further, Doreen had invited the couple to lunch.

Now, as Doreen resumed the conversation about Joel's concerns, he lifted his palm to stop her. "What I just saw makes me understand," he said, referring to Esmeralda's exchange with Doreen. "Now I have confidence that Silverado will love and care for Melanie as much as I do." Joel reached over and took his wife's hand in one of his. With the other, he pulled a handkerchief from his pocket and dabbed at his eyes.

For more than a decade, Andrea had cultivated customers and closed deals in the automotive industry. Eager to hone her business skills, she moved on to become a loan officer and a real estate agent. With the recession weighing heavily on those sectors, she began plotting her next career move and landed an interview for a managerial position at a conference center.

On the way home from the meeting, a sign caught her eye: "Silverado Senior Living, Care for People with Alzheimer's Disease and Other Memory Impairments."

"I wonder if they have any openings," she thought.

The silent question startled the woman who had always carved her achievements in numbers and transactions. She braked, turned into the driveway, and parked. Andrea hadn't set foot in a senior care community since her childhood, when she was taken to visit elderly relatives in a nursing home. She had no experience, professional or personal, with memory impairment – and no idea what to expect as she opened the front door to Silverado.

She discovered sparkling lights, greenery, and music filling the foyer. People were grouped on plush couches and easy chairs, some chatting, others absorbed in the melodies heralding the approaching holidays.

"It took my breath away," Andrea recalled later. "It was beautiful. I could feel so much warmth."

Andrea crossed to the reception desk, introduced herself, and asked whether there were any staff openings.

"You are welcome to take a seat and someone will be right out to speak with you," she was told. Andrea sat on a divan near the Christmas tree, next to a white-haired man. He turned and smiled at her.

"What's your name?" he asked.

"Andrea," she said. "What's yours?"

"George," he replied. Then he smiled again. "You are a beautiful woman." George spoke the compliment from the heart. His sincerity and sweetness moved Andrea deeply.

In that instant, Andrea couldn't have put a name to what had just happened. But it meant something, she was certain.

As it turned out, Silverado had no openings that fit her experience, but they were looking for a caregiver. Andrea heard herself say, "I would like to apply." And she was hired. It was clear to those at Silverado that, like Esmeralda, Andrea possessed what was most important – compassion.

The first few weeks were nerve-wracking. She constantly wondered what she had gotten herself into. Being a caregiver was demanding in a way that her most hectic days in business had never been. The first time she was called upon to help a male resident in the bathroom was a shock.

"I needed to stop thinking about how the task was affecting me. I needed to focus on how important it was to make the resident feel dignified and comfortable in what must have been a very difficult situation for him."

Soon, Andrea began telling family and friends how much she enjoyed the work. Everyday, she came home exhausted, but elated, by having conjured a smile, a laugh, or a conversation out of a resident. She was certain those around her must have tired of hearing her enthusiastic daily descriptions of Silverado.

As each day passed, the idea of managing a memory care community's daily operations naturally appealed more and more to the businesswoman in Andrea. With Silverado's support, she obtained certification for an administrator's license in California and eventually moved to Illinois where she went on to mentor new Silverado administrators as they joined the organization.

When Andrea first walked into Silverado, the environment of love drew her. It guided her past the anxiety of stepping out of a familiar career path to venture into the unknown. Several years after the conversation with George in the foyer, she sees that when she connected with the spirit of a memory-impaired person for the first time, it changed her life. *Love is greater than fear.*

Loren Shook and Steve Winner believe that if other dementia care organizations operated on Silverado's love-based principle, significant strides would be made toward solving the shortage of caregivers predicted for the surge of aging baby boomers.

"There are so many people who have an innate desire to care for the frail elderly, but they can't find a place to truly do that," Steve Winner said. "Employees who come to Silverado from other senior care organizations often say that here, they're free to provide the kind of care they've always wanted to offer: care that's entirely about residents and their families. The sole duty of caregivers at Silverado is just that: hands-on care. They are not "universal workers," who are expected to perform other kinds of duties as well."

Applicants to Silverado are tested and interviewed for high levels of compassion. Many employees come to Silverado with a background unrelated to health care. While they lack experience in caregiving, they have the exceptional empathy Silverado seeks.

For some staff members, the opportunity to provide compassionate care to Silverado's residents is transformational, giving positive meaning to their own earlier experiences. Esmeralda, the caregiver whose childhood was marked by her father's alcoholism and loss of caring relationships, believes her intuitive understanding of other people's feelings comes from those hardships. She says she is certain that "it is my purpose to help others. It is a calling from God. He made me this way and this is what He wants me to do."

Resident engagement director Dottie never knew her mother and lost her father when she was six. As a result, she grew up in a girls' home. One day, Dottie and the other girls were taken to visit nursing homes as a community service project.

"I was drawn to the residents," Dottie says. "I could see the love they were lacking, and I was lacking love, too. Being able to give them love filled the void in me."

In her teens, she became a certified nursing assistant and later began handling activities in a convalescent home. "Coming to Silverado," she says, "with its *Love is greater than fear* principle has been an awesome experience. It enables me to express myself by caring for the residents. It gives me purpose and meaning."

Gloria struggled with obesity and lack of confidence until she lost a hundred pounds in her early thirties. The achievement gave her fresh self-esteem and focus. Becoming a personal trainer and massage therapist, she discovered "a passion for helping people to be the best they can be."

After the Illinois spa where she worked closed, she pursued a longtime dream of living in a warm climate. Renting a 27-foot-truck, she attached her car to the back and drove to Arizona to build a new life. When she learned that Silverado needed an engagement assistant, she applied. Although she had no experience, her obvious compassion secured her the position.

"Here, you are allowed to work with your heart," said Gloria, now a resident engagement director. "I came to Silverado thinking I was going to help other people, and I quickly realized that I was the one being helped by the wonderful experiences with the residents every day."

Silverado retains staff at a far higher rate than the long-term care industry's notoriously low average. The corrosive impact of constant employee turnover on the quality of care is well documented, as is the nation's caregiver shortage. The main reasons people abandon the field are 1) a lack of respect for the position of caregiver, 2) scant training, and 3) poor opportunities for advancement. The Silverado approach addresses all three.

With compassion as the primary hiring attribute, the rest falls into place. Silverado trains all new hires in its own techniques. Topics such as Alzheimer's disease, dementia, and infection control are naturally part of the curriculum, but so are Silverado's core philosophies and practices, including the principle of *Love is greater than fear.*

New staff members are paired with mentors who work side-by-side with them until they are ready to handle their duties on their own. Since acquiring new knowledge and career advancement are primary values at Silverado, staff members are encouraged to participate in a wide range of training programs. The company's affiliated nonprofit foundation also offers tuition assistance to employees seeking careers in long-term care.

"The extensive training not only benefits staff, it also allows Silverado to maintain the consistent quality of its care as it has grown over the years," observes Dr. Joe W. Ramsdell. "The comprehensive, ongoing education of all employees means each person understands and supports Silverado's care mission."

Silverado's *Love is greater than fear* principle frees staff members to devote themselves to residents because they know they will never be criticized for doing what is best for those in their care.

Act from your heart.

Provide the kind of care you yearn to give.

Do it always.

These tenets provide a special quality of caregiving and ensures that everyone in Silverado's care has a consistent experience regardless of how large the company becomes.

Silverado's total staff ratios are among the best in the industry. Overall staffing at a Silverado community is typically one FTE staff member per resident (full-time equivalent is one or more staff whose time totals a 40-hour work week). It is the rare provider that comes close to this, although many will say they have more caregivers. This is because other care providers have what they call "universal caregivers" who do a variety of non-caregiving tasks such as housekeeping and culinary work. Silverado caregivers are dedicated to one thing – caregiving. Silverado also has staff others do not usually have, such as on-site licensed nurses 24/7, a fully-staffed engagement department, a masters-level social worker, and a leadership team that freely engages with residents and their families. Since Silverado caregivers have a full support team cleaning, cooking, etc., they can dedicate as much time as they need to each person under their care. Other unique features, such as a shift overlap of half an hour, allow caregivers and nurses on one shift to provide information and recommendations about each resident's condition to oncoming staff, improving important communication.

Silverado fosters an environment of celebration to highlight its love-based resident-centered care mission. Everyone who is part of the Silverado community, whether resident, associate, or family member, is encouraged to fill out "Caught You Caring" slips posted on bulletin boards for all to see. They cite individual employees for great work with a resident or interaction with other staff.

Employees also write up and circulate "Silverado Success Stories" throughout the organization, recounting details of exceptional care.

In another Silverado Success Story, a resident of Silverado At Home saluted staff for keeping him alive by helping him learn to walk and feed himself again. Yet another describes how a Silverado caregiver calmed the grief of a newly widowed woman by taking her hand and stepping outside with her to see the beauty of moonlight on water as they shared tears and silence.

These success stories encourage associates to develop creative ways to enhance care. Allison, a Silverado Hospice administrator, enjoys therapeutic personal massage. Noticing how lavender oil soothed her after a stressful day, Allison wondered whether it could alleviate symptoms and discomfort for Silverado's patients, potentially reducing or eliminating the need to use certain drugs. Surveying her patients and their families, she found they were eager to find non-medication relief for pain, agitation, itching, and depression. Allison's research identified marjoram, bergamot, sandalwood, and lavender as possibly helpful in addressing those problems. Using those oils, she began blending lotions, customizing them to individual patients. For example, a woman with Lou Gehrig's disease who suffered from severe neck and jaw pain could not speak and had to be fed with a syringe. Not liking to take pain medications, she welcomed this alternative. Combinations of lavender and marjoram in both oil and mist form eased her pain to the point that she no longer needed to take prescription pain pills or sleep aids.

Loren Shook's and Steve Winner's love-based approach also provides guidance for the interaction of employees with one another. That is, "Choose your actions and words from the standpoint of love and what's best in each situation, rather than from fear of potentially negative consequences." Setting aside worries about rejection and ridicule, they can reach out with kind words that bring fresh richness to relationships.

Angel, a chef at one of Silverado's memory care communities, recalls that when she was introduced to the *Love is greater than fear* principle during an orientation, she thought it was far-fetched. Since her previous career had been in the restaurant and catering business, it was hard to view a work environment as anything but cutthroat.

It began to make sense to her when she used the principle to handle a problem with a kitchen employee. Angel's normal style was to announce mandates tersely and hope they would be followed. When her tactic had no effect, the administrator of her Silverado community suggested that she change her approach to *Love is greater than fear*. Instead of issuing a command, Angel should ask the employee, "What can I do for you that would make completing your tasks easier?" or "I want to work with you to help you be successful."

The impact was gratifying. A conversation between Angel and the employee about how they could cooperate in the future improved the relationship immensely. As Angel saw the effects of *Love is greater than fear* in the workplace, she began to embrace the philosophy in her family life. Ultimately, it dramatically improved her tense relationship with her father. "Recently," she related, "I wrote a letter to my father and used the word 'love' for the first time. I'm more open now to think about what I can do to help make a situation more positive.

For over two decades, Joe worked six days a week at his restaurant and deli. From morning to evening, he welcomed customers, supervised employees, balanced the books, and made sure the cuisine was up to standards. Approaching his twenty-third year in the business, he decided to sell the thriving enterprise and retire.

While he was driving on an errand two years later, he noticed a sign for Silverado. Joe had no experience with memory care, either in his career or in his personal life. It wasn't something he'd thought about much. But he found himself pulling into the parking lot, going to the front desk, and asking, "What can I do to help the people at Silverado?"

Joe was hired as an engagement assistant and he plunged into the job, launching the community's classical music club. Before each gathering, Joe researches and chooses pieces to feature. At the meetings, he makes his presentation, serves sparkling cider for participants to sip as they listen to the music, and then they discuss the day's selections.

The residents' responses to the music touch him deeply. A smile by a previously somber woman or an insightful comment from a normally taciturn gentleman affects him in ways he never considered. "When I leave at the end of the day, I'm drained but also uplifted. It is so important to engage each resident every day. That's why I am here."

Loren Shook did not know Joe then, but he understands the reason Joe was drawn to Silverado. "There are so many accomplished people in a wide variety of fields who want to do something with purpose in retirement. If care organizations gave them an environment of love and creativity where they can feel the joy of helping others every day, we would see more people choosing to work with the memory impaired."

Chapter Fourteen

The Family's Experience

In the sweetness of friendship let there be laughter and sharing of pleasures.
For in the dew of little things the heart finds its morning and is refreshed.

– Kahlil Gibran

At Silverado, providing attention and assistance to the families of the memory impaired is as important as serving the people directly in its care. Ever since its founding, the organization has offered support groups for relatives and friends.

"How is everyone feeling?" Werner asked. There was a long silence. Then Russell spoke up.

"It's lonely." Werner leaned forward slightly in encouragement and Russell began to speak again.

"I've been in the house by myself for three months now, and I'm still not used to it. Now that Meredith is at Silverado, I'm getting a full night's sleep. So, from a physical standpoint, I guess I'm doing better." Russell paused. "But I feel alone."

Around the table, heads nodded. Philip, Gary, Bert, Vernon and the rest: they understood.

For almost every person on the odyssey of Alzheimer's or another memory-impairing disease, there is a spouse or family member also walking a new, unaccustomed path. The final destination for the memory impaired is sadly known. What lies over the horizon for those on the other trail – the husbands, wives, companions, and adult children – is less obvious. But evident to anyone who has ever taken this unwanted trip is that it is laden with visceral emotions and milestones. For spouses and long-time partners, there is the added uncertainty of how to refashion a life no longer clearly defined.

This was why Werner was leading a group discussion among nine men whose spouses were residents at Silverado. During the twelve months that Lucette, Werner's wife of sixty years, resided at Silverado, he visited her 340 days. Making friends with the residents and staff, he participated in the family support group and came to view Silverado as an extension of his home. Even after Lucette passed away, he continued to stop in. One day, Veronica, the community's director of resident and family services, asked him if he would be willing to spearhead a new support group.

"It would be for men only. There are a number of men whose wives are residing here who might find it easier to talk about what they're going through if there weren't any ladies present."

Werner thought for a moment. "I'll be happy to try it if you think it would be worthwhile. Of course, you know that I've never run a support group."

Veronica smiled, "I'm certain you will know what to do."

Shortly thereafter, Werner gamely reported to Silverado for the first meeting in his new role. He had reflected quite a bit since his conversation with Veronica. As a retired international banker, he had decades of experience running meetings, sometimes in more than one language. He thought the skills he honed in all those years might be helpful now.

Caregiving is a stressful job in most situations. Studies have shown that husbands caring for ailing wives are at the highest risk of having a stroke.

The men had lunch first to relax the atmosphere. Then Werner cleared his throat and asked the question about how everyone was feeling. The ensuing silence sent a flicker of anxiety through Werner. What if the men found it too hard to discuss personal matters? But after Russell spoke of his loneliness, Vernon jumped in.

"I know what you mean. It's strange realizing that Jessica will never be in the bed beside me again. Often when I wake up, I think at first that she got up for a few minutes to go into the bathroom and that she'll be right back," Vernon said. He took a sip of water and continued. "In the last few months that Jessica lived at home, I moved into the guest room. She started thrashing a lot during the night, and I wasn't getting any rest. But no bed ever felt as empty as my bed feels now."

When Vernon finished his comments, everyone remained quiet. Werner prepared to pose another question. But then Bert said:

"I understand what you're saying. I've been by myself for more than a year now, and my children think I am doing fine. I guess in a lot of ways, I am, but missing their mother in bed isn't something I'm going to mention to them." Rueful smiles and a few knowing chuckles greeted Bert's remarks.

In the hour that followed, Werner found that, indeed, the men spoke of intimate issues. Perhaps, he thought, it was the first time they had felt at liberty to do so. They came from varying walks of life, but they had in common the male mask of stoicism. They had worn this visage while coping with the changes memory impairment had wrought on the women they cherished – sudden crying jags, anger, hurtful language, and the need for help in the bathroom. Many of the men had weathered these new behaviors for years, as they cared for their spouses at home. Each had reached the point that his ability to provide care was not sufficient for his wife's needs, but they had never spoken to anyone about their pain, which Werner now understood ranged from anguish to depression.

As the initial session wrapped up, the men made it clear they wanted the group to continue. Now, Werner leads the males-only luncheon once every three months. It's been more than a year since his wife's passing, and he is in a different phase from the other men, who still grapple with their wives' memory impairment as part of their daily lives.

"I have gone through the whole cycle, from the beginning of my wife's symptoms to the end," Werner says. "I know that one of the hardest things for a spouse is that you don't know where this is going, what to expect." He recalls that when the men got together that first day, they started to make comparisons of their situations. They found comfort, understanding, and advice.

Werner is a busy man these days; he not only consults on international banking, he also travels, skis, reads, and spends time with his daughter.

"I feel guilty sometimes because of all the things I enjoy now, without my wife here," he says in a soft voice. "But I understand that life does go on and you have a certain responsibility to live it."

Ken was shocked the first time the police came to the house and wanted to set up a command post.

"My mother is missing. She didn't rob a bank."

At fifty-two, Ken was not leading the life he had imagined for himself. He did not foresee having to summon the authorities to search for his mother Marilyn, not just once, but frequently over a period of years. Nor did he anticipate having to explain to her over and over again that she was no longer allowed to drive. Every time Marilyn asked for her car keys, her anger and sorrow were fresh, as though she had just learned the news. And Ken never imagined leaving his career for part-time work because his mother's needs took so much of his time.

"I've always been close to my mother," says Ken. "Despite a difficult marriage, she raised us three boys with grace. We always knew we could count on her. Now the roles are reversed. Being a caregiver teaches you how to really love someone. You embrace what 'honor thy father and mother' truly means. When all this is over, I will be able to say I tried my best."

When Marilyn was 77 she moved to Silverado, and Ken became a regular participant at Silverado's monthly support groups. He finds that talking about his experience helps.

"As a caregiver, you experience a lot of isolation. You feel like you're watching the rest of the world go by, and you're in a completely different place, having a completely different experience. With the support group, you know you're not the only one. Hearing what others have learned over the years brings perspective. It's an ongoing reinforcement process for what you're doing and feeling.

Each week for six months, six women gathered in a local sewing shop to create a quilt. Some had never wielded a needle and thread before, but they were determined to learn. Each woman was creating a square to honor her husband. For Bruce, the square's theme would be football, a sport he played in his youth. A rose would represent Diane's husband, Tom; he had planted a rose garden at every home they lived during their 50-year marriage.

Each of the women had joined Silverado's family support group, and for the first time had met other wives who had long cared for their husbands at home. As they constructed their quilt, they stitched together new friendships to sustain them through the loss of their spouses to memory impairment.

"What I was going through with Bruce was something I just didn't talk about with other people," said Bette. Her husband's condition was diagnosed three years before he came to Silverado. As his dementia progressed, he became verbally and physically aggressive, a situation Bette endured because of her love for him and the firm belief in the vow she had taken for better or for worse.

When she finally admitted she could not handle Bruce's care at home any more, he moved to Silverado. Bette felt defeated, as though she had failed everyone in the family. Then, a simple exchange with another support group participant changed her life. The woman quietly confided to the group that her husband had been aggressive at home. Bette drew in her breath in surprise and said, "You, too?" The two looked at each other with understanding. It was the beginning of liberation from the guilt, sorrow, anger, and isolation that each had felt for so long.

Even when their adult children could not comprehend what caring for their memory-impaired fathers had been like, these new friends understood, didn't criticize their feelings or decisions, and offered unwavering solidarity. "When one woman was feeling depressed, the rest of us were able to lift her spirits and comfort her," said Diane.

Giving voice to emotions and regaining a perspective which had been lost in the stress of daily caregiving allowed Bette to fall in love with her husband again. She said, "When you're a full time caregiver at home with a difficult person, you can forget how many years of your marriage were actually wonderful."

All the women relished the weekly stitching sessions. They laughed and experienced the satisfying sense of working alongside others to create something that mattered. When the project concluded and the quilt was displayed on the wall at Silverado, the women began considering their next group project. "We don't want to let go of each other."

Chapter Fifteen

Hospice with Love

Namaste: I honor the place in you where the entire universe resides; I honor that place within you of love, of light, of truth, of peace; I honor the place in you where, when you are in that place in you and I am in that place in me, there is only one of us.

– Mahatma Gandhi

In her mid-twenties, Kathleen donned white overalls every day and assembled .50 caliber machine gun bullets for the troops fighting in World War II. At the end of her shift, she pulled off the overalls, dropped them in the factory laundry bin, and showered to remove the dangerous gunpowder that inevitably clung to her after hours of handling ammunition.

In her free time, she learned how to fly. She was one of the few women to take the private-pilot course at the tiny airstrip nearby. One day, she put a plane into a practice-stall above a pasture. As the aircraft began to fall, she restarted the engine, leveled the aircraft, and took in a sharp breath. She hadn't noticed the electric lines stretching along the edge of the field. Not sure the plane had enough power to quickly thrust upward, Kathleen flew below the lines and made a safe landing at the airport.

Now 85 and living in her son's suburban home, Kathleen could not fathom that the stairs were too dangerous for her. She had been confined to a bedroom on the second floor for weeks and it was making her stir-crazy. She wanted to be part of the family.

The home health aide had chided, "It's too risky. You're too weak to manage the steps."

True, she had Parkinson's disease and a defective heart valve, but it hadn't been that long since she had pushed a boogie board into a cove off Maui with her grandson Aaron on one side and her son on the other. Kathleen couldn't swim any more, but she could look through the plastic viewer in the boogie board to see the aquatic life below. That was as close to snorkeling as she was going to get. Now two aides from a local hospice service hovered over her, preventing her from even going down stairs.

Seeing her so stifled, her son arranged for a new caregiver to come to the house, this one trained by Silverado.

"I want to go downstairs," Kathleen told the young woman in no uncertain terms.

The caregiver nodded and replied, "I think I have an idea."

That afternoon when her son returned from work, Kathleen was on the couch in the first-floor family room, a grandchild on either side, all three laughing. When she caught her son's eye, her smile conveyed joy, along with a small measure of "I told you so."

It was true that Kathleen could no longer safely navigate the stairs. With assistance, however, she could sit on the top step and descend the stairs on her backside.

"If you can't fly over the power lines, go under them," Kathleen told her son.

Kathleen's son was Loren Shook.

In early 2003, doctors determined Loren's mother Kathleen was in the last six months of her life and recommended hospice services. At that time, Silverado was in the planning stages of its own hospice program and homecare services. Having been intimately involved in the process, Loren thought he knew what to expect when the local hospice sent aides to his house to care for his own mother.

He soon found that researching hospice was one thing; experiencing it was another. The aides were conscientious in giving medications, helping Kathleen bathe, and handling other standard duties. What they lacked was feeling; they made little effort to get to know her as a person and to understand her motivation. In Loren's opinion, this aspect of healthcare was fundamental, whether hospice, home care, assisted living, or hospital. The Silverado associate who devised the way for Kathleen to go down the stairs understood her yearning for freedom and accomplishment. Rather than discourage Kathleen, the associate focused on how to help her fulfill her desires.

When hospice personnel told Loren his mother had entered into "active dying," that is, that her death was imminent, he was shocked that the hospice nurse would not stay throughout the process. It was against company policy. Only several outraged calls by Loren to the service's top management yielded a reversal of that stance. The memory of having to take the time and energy to badger the hospice administrators at such a difficult time still bothers him.

Because of the nature of Alzheimer's and many other dementias, the end of life occurs for almost all Silverado residents at its communities. Most receive hospice care, a service recommended by health professionals when an individual is determined to have entered the final six months of life. Previously, outside hospice organizations had come to Silverado to work side by side with Silverado caregivers. But the Silverado staff were in hearty agreement, "We could do this ourselves so much better. We need to offer hospice."

Loren's experience with the adequate but dispassionate care provided to his mother made him realize what they were talking about: the act of dying is a significant part of a life. Silverado's mission of nurturing the spirit to the fullest extent needed to be carried on until the very last moments.

As a result, Silverado's mission would not just be to exceed current standards of hospice care, but to create an environment that enabled people to experience death on their own terms. The new Silverado Hospice would take into consideration the remaining possibilities for their lives, with the ultimate goal of providing self-satisfaction and a sense of completeness to individuals and their loved ones.

Love is greater than fear is Silverado's core operating principle. It is especially relevant for Silverado Hospice, where patients, families, and associates are confronting what frightens people most: imminent mortality. Fear of death keeps society from talking about it. Fear keeps individuals from planning for it. And all too often, fear keeps those approaching the end of life from connecting with the world around them.

Silverado has identified four objectives for their hospice program. The first is normalization. The concept of normalization for people with dementia has been central to Silverado from the start, so extending it to include people without dementia at the end of life was only natural. Normalization enables hospice patients to enjoy the daily routines and diversions that are standard for all adults, regardless of the anticipated date of passing away. Normal activities include getting out of bed and dressing in the morning to participate in pastimes of personal interest. Why exclude hospice patients from reasonable activities at this time of life? Telling a dying woman like Loren's mother that going down a flight of stairs was too dangerous limited her spirit as she sought to stay connected to the world. As she demonstrated, there is dignity, purpose, and fulfillment in risk when handled in the right way.

The second objective of Silverado's hospice program is making the most of life: Pleasure and purpose are meaningful at any stage of life, but vitally important in the final stage. Silverado Hospice endeavors to bring enjoyment and focus to each day. In addition, Silverado honors and preserves individual life experiences through the Memory Catcher Program, in which patients are interviewed on video about their lives and are given the opportunity to express important thoughts and feelings for their loved ones to remember.

The third objective is guiding patients and families through the end-of-life process: When illness starts to diminish the quality of life, feelings of uncertainty can be overwhelming. Silverado works with those in its care as well as their loved ones to explain what is taking place and what is likely to transpire. Further, it strives to identify and fulfill individual preferences and to bring the patient and the family to the same understanding.

Using the Go Wish™ program, Silverado encourages patients to pinpoint what matters most to them at the end of life and to indicate if there is anything special they would like to achieve at this time. For example, they may wish to limit pain medication in order to be as alert as possible; or they may have "unfinished business," such as family estrangements they would like to mend. Once Silverado identifies end-of-life wishes, the staff strives to make them a reality.

After the patient's life has ended, Silverado assists families and friends in coping with the grieving process, offering a wide range of bereavement groups and one-on-one counseling. Participants may attend for as long as they wish. The groups are open to anyone who would like to take part, regardless of whether they have been a Silverado client.

The fourth objective of Silverado's hospice program is connecting with the human spirit, no matter how hidden it may seem. People whose loved ones have Alzheimer's disease can understandably be shaken by the loss of faculties. When the patient can no longer recognize a spouse, child, or close friend and can no longer communicate with intelligible speech, it can seem to the family that the patient died even before hospice began. But Silverado, sensitive to those feelings, continues to make sustaining the spirit of the memory-impaired person an important focus for the hospice team.

Spiritual care coordinators from a variety of faiths understand and agree that their responsibility at Silverado Hospice is to create an atmosphere that leads to spiritual encounter and growth. The connection does not have to be based on religion, although it can be if that is what the patient wishes.

One spiritual care coordinator calls Silverado's approach "sacred presence," the very description suggesting that each visit to a patient is like entering sacred space. An unresponsive patient is greeted with no less expectation than the most alert and verbal patient.

To the best of Silverado's ability, no one will die alone. When the process of active dying starts, staff is in constant communication with families, so they can be present if that is what the patient and loved one desires. Silverado also provides a continuing personal presence, committed to being physically and emotionally available for the patient and family at all times.

"You're here to put me in a nursing home, aren't you?" Mandy said, eyeing Libbie with suspicion. "That's why you keep coming around; don't think I don't know it." Mandy, a woman in her fifties, was angry and in despair over her terminal illness. Though pale from cancer that could no longer be controlled and too weak to rise on her own from her living room couch, Mandy's voice still carried with startling force: "I'm not going."

"No, that's not why I'm here," Libbie protested as she leaned forward in the easy chair facing Mandy. "We all know you want to stay at home. I'm as committed to that as everyone else on our team." Mandy looked skeptical. In the three years since her illness had been discovered, various healthcare professionals had told Mandy her increasing needs would make moving to a nursing home inevitable. Recently, Silverado Hospice had begun caring for her in the white stucco home she shared with her husband, Jeff. As a Silverado Hospice social worker, Libbie was part of the care team. But her presence clearly alarmed Mandy.

"I've talked to social workers before, and they've all told me I would have to go," Mandy said.

"I understand your concern," Libbie said. "But believe me; I will do all I can so you can remain right here."

It took more discussion, at times heated on Mandy's part, to convince her of Libbie's purpose on the Hospice team, which was to focus on the psychological and emotional well-being of Mandy and her family. Providing this kind of assistance to others in the last stages of their lives gave Libbie the meaning she was searching for when she left her interior design career to pursue social work.

Once Mandy's fears were allayed, she and Libbie turned to chatting casually. It was the kind of conversation that two women anywhere could have had, and it brought a comfortable normality to the situation. When Mandy's attention was turned toward things she could still look forward to, it helped greatly.

In a previous conversation, Libbie had asked Mandy what was on her bucket list. When Mandy said she didn't have one, Libbie had encouraged her to think about what she'd like to do and to write it down. Her response had been noncommittal.

Now Mandy said, "I haven't told anyone, but I did make that list you talked about."

"Oh, that's wonderful," Libbie said. "What's on it?"

"Well, this and that," Mandy said.

Libbie could tell that even with their new understanding of each other, Mandy wasn't yet sure how much she wanted to share. But by mentioning the list, Mandy had created an opening on an important subject. Libbie knew it was crucial to respond in just the right way.

"Could you tell me what's at the top of the list?" she asked gently. "If we can help you make it happen, we'd be honored." Mandy was quiet for a few moments, long enough for Libbie to notice the grandfather clock in the corner ticking loudly.

Finally, Mandy said, "I'd like to have a Red Lobster dinner." Her illness had prevented her from eating anything rich for a long time. Libbie checked with Mandy's physician and was given the all clear, so she began working on the arrangements. Libbie knew that Mandy would be too frail to go to a crowded restaurant, and takeout wasn't available. When Silverado's home office contacted Red Lobster headquarters to explain the situation, the company offered to send two employees with the food to Mandy's home, free of charge.

That evening, Libbie and a pair of Silverado Hospice volunteers set a table with linens, silver, and china for Mandy and her husband, Jeff, to enjoy the fare in elegance.

After the couple finished dinner, Mandy said, "I never explained why I wanted this."

Lifting a hand to her cheek to wipe away a tear, Mandy continued, "It was during dinner at Red Lobster ten years ago that Jeff first told me he loved me."

A few days later, Mandy confided to Libbie that their wedding had been a civil ceremony with a justice of the peace. Another wish on her list was to exchange vows with Jeff in the Catholic cathedral in their city of Houston. Libbie agreed to try to arrange it, but she knew pulling off a ceremony in a short amount of time could stump even the most seasoned of wedding planners. When she called the cathedral, she wasn't surprised to learn it was booked solid for weddings for the next 18 months.

"But to be sure," Libbie coaxed the scheduler, "could you double-check the third Saturday of next month?"

Doubtful but willing, the scheduler placed Libbie on hold for a few minutes. When he returned to the line, he said, "This is amazing. I don't know how or why, but the afternoon of that day is available. If you'd like it, it's yours."

Details began falling into place. As the result of a news report on the special dinner and her wish for a cathedral ceremony, a florist called offering arrangements, bouquets, and decorations for free. Not long after, a photographer offered her services at no charge. People across the city wanted to help Mandy. Libbie's phone continued to ring. A bakery, a wedding gown shop, a hairstylist, and a make-up artist all volunteered as well.

On the day of the wedding, Mandy, clad in a three-quarter length white dress and holding a red and white bouquet, rolled into the cathedral in a wheelchair wreathed with fresh white flowers and greenery. White gauze cascaded along its sides. Arriving at the aisle, Mandy insisted on stopping and held out her arm to the man pushing the chair. The guests gasped as Mandy put her hand on the man's forearm and stood. The pair began walking toward the altar where Jeff was waiting. Mandy moved haltingly and over one shoulder she carried the portable oxygen unit feeding the tubes hooked to her nose. But she had a grace that any bride would envy.

Terra lived with her grandparents from age nine to eighteen and was a constant visitor in their home in the decades that followed. Merle, her grandmother, was her inspiration and role model.

At Silverado, Terra was a volunteer coordinator and manager of the Memory Catcher Program. By recording video interviews, she obtained unique histories of patients' lives and helped preserve personal messages to family and friends. When her grandmother entered the care of Silverado Hospice, the program became very personal for Terra.

One morning, she set up a video camera across from Merle and took a seat facing her.

"Grandma, could you please tell me the story one more time?"

"You want to hear it again?" Merle responded in the warm teasing tone Terra knew so well.

"Yes, from the very beginning," Terra said. "Tell me the whole thing."

Merle didn't have to ask her granddaughter which story she meant. Terra had begged over and over to hear the tale since she was six-years-old.

"Well," Merle began, "I was thirteen years old. There was a new girl at school and we became friends. One day, she and I were having a snack in her kitchen, and her brother Jerry came in." She stopped, as she customarily did at this point.

"What was he like?" Terra asked. Merle smiled. Terra always asked that question; it was part of the story's ritual.

"At first, I didn't pay him any mind," Merle chuckled. "But he kept standing there leaning against the icebox, and I got the feeling he was watching me. So I turned to look at him, and guess what?" She paused again.

"What?" said Terra, as expected.

"He had the most beautiful eyes I had ever seen," Merle said.

Over the next two months, Jerry barely said more than hello when they ran into each other during her visits to the house. But he secretly badgered his sister for more information about her friend, and Merle likewise tried to get details about him. When Jerry finally gathered his nerve and invited Merle out for an ice cream sundae, it took just that one date for them to realize they were meant for each other.

While she was still in high school, Merle bought her wedding dress, but the couple's plans to marry after graduation were stymied by World War II. Jerry was drafted. Sent to the South Pacific, he was chosen to be part of a group working with a new technology called radar. For four years, Jerry and Merle didn't see each other, but Merle never so much as looked at another man during that time.

Merle took another pause.

"Why?" Terra asked as anticipated. "Why were you willing to wait so long for Grandpa when you could have been dating other boys?"

"Because I loved him," Merle said.

Reaching over and covering Merle's hand with hers, Terra asked, "If you could tell Grandpa anything, what would you want him to know?"

Not once in the decades since Terra first heard the story had she asked Merle that question, but the change in ritual didn't surprise her grandmother. Merle and Terra understood that sharing the story this time was different.

"I would want Jerry to know that I love him," Merle answered.

Devastated as Terra was when Merle passed away four weeks later, she knew it was worse for Jerry, also a Silverado Hospice patient.

Three months after Merle's death, when Terra felt strong enough to bring up the subject without crying, she said to Jerry, "Grandpa, if you could, would you want to see Grandma again?"

"Oh, honey, of course I would," he replied. "If only it were possible. I would want that more than anything."

Terra's laptop was on the small table in front of Jerry, and her headphones covered his ears. She leaned across his lap to click an icon on the computer, willing herself to appear calm, not knowing how her grandfather would react.

As Merle's face suddenly filled the screen, Jerry's eyes widened. Tears welling, he drew a short breath as her mouth began moving. He stretched out his hand to touch the computer. Caressing Merle's image, Jerry smiled for the first time since her passing.

Jenna, a Silverado Hospice social worker, accompanied 85-year-old Randall onto the patio of his skilled nursing facility. An aide helped him from his wheelchair into a cushioned wicker seat while Jenna adjusted an umbrella to provide shade.

"It's beautiful out here," she told the aide. "Will you come back for us in an hour?"

"Certainly," he said. The aide went into the building, and Jenna pulled a chair over so she could face Randall.

Eight months earlier, Parkinson's disease had brought Randall to the nursing facility. Although he was able to stand, he could no longer walk. Recently, doctors had determined that the end of his life was approaching. Silverado Hospice, which often provides services to patients at other senior living centers, started visiting him.

This man, whose engaging smile was undimmed by illness, had captivated Jenna. When Randall had said he was eager for winter weather to end so he could go out in the fresh air, Jenna began keeping an eye on the forecast. With warm sunshine expected for this day, she blocked the afternoon on her calendar with the word "Randall."

After he settled into his seat with a sigh of pleasure, she leaned toward him.

"Randall, there's a question I'd like to ask you," she began.

"All right," he said.

"I am wondering whether there are some things you might like to accomplish in the next few months," she said.

"Hmm," Randall said. "It's not something I've thought about."

"That's fine," Jenna said reassuringly. "But I'd like to suggest that you consider it. At this phase of life, it's important to think about whether there are things left undone or unsaid. If there are, there's still time to accomplish them." He looked at her, but didn't say anything.

"If you'd like, I could help you think about it," she said. "Would that be all right?" When he nodded, Jenna said, "Give me a moment." She stood and brought a small table over to set down between their two chairs. Then she sat and reached into her handbag to pull out a deck of cards.

"We aren't going to play poker," she said with a smile in response to Randall's obvious surprise. "This is a game called Go Wish™."

Jenna explained that the cards contained things that people often say are important to them in the final stage of life. She would read each card aloud to Randall. Then, he was to tell her whether it was "Very important to me," "Somewhat important to me," or "Not important to me."

Randall nodded again, so Jenna shuffled the deck and turned the top card over.

"To have my family with me,'" she read. "Randall, is that very important, somewhat important, or not important to you?"

"Very important," he said. Jenna placed the card face down on the table and read the next one:

"To say goodbye to important people in my life."

"Not important," Randall said. "Well, what I mean is that they all already know how I feel about them."

She put the card on the table a short distance from the first one. Then she turned another card over.

"To feel my life is complete." Randall's expression became thoughtful and a few moments passed. She broke the silence by saying, "Randall, I noticed there's a model airplane on your nightstand. Who built it?"

A slow smile spread across Randall's face. "I did," he said.

"When?" she asked.

"A long time ago," he answered.

He was fifteen then, he explained. For three weeks, he spent every waking hour outside of school and chores building the tiny aircraft to enter in a competition sponsored by the local newspaper. When he received a letter from the judges, he had to read it three times before believing he had won the top prize: a free plane ride. It was his first-ever flight.

In World War II, Randall was chosen to pilot a B-25 Mitchell bomber. At the war's end, he became a firefighter for 38 years and also served as an airport paramedic. In his spare time, he taught flying lessons, once flying a two-seater the length of the Grand Canyon. He had also climbed almost every peak in Utah's Uinta Mountains, saying "It was as close as possible to being in the air while still on land."

"What did your wife think about your flying?" Jenna asked him.

"Sharon encouraged it," Randall said. "She always said I wouldn't be myself without it." He smiled and continued, "You know, I flew her across the Uintas on our second date. I would have done it on our first date, but I didn't want to scare her off." They both laughed.

Then Jenna said, "So, the card I read to you a little while ago – the one that says 'To feel my life is complete.' If you could, would you want to fly over those mountains with Sharon one more time?"

"Oh, yes," Randall said without hesitation. "That would be more important than anything."

It took a number of phone calls, but Jenna found a pilot willing to fly the couple over the mountain range. When she explained that Randall's wish followed a lifelong passion for flying, he said he would be honored to do it at no charge. The date the pilot was available was Randall and Sharon's fifty-eighth wedding anniversary. Jenna and her Silverado Hospice colleagues arranged for a van to transport Randall and Sharon to and from the airport and for a nurse to be on hand in case Randall needed medical attention.

Alerted by Silverado Hospice, two airport firefighters were waiting as the van pulled up to the four-seat Cessna.

"That's my favorite plane!" Randall exclaimed as he was lowered to his wheelchair.

As the firefighters approached to assist him into the plane, he gestured for them to wait. Only after rising slowly to his feet did he take their arms. While Sharon stepped up into the plane and settled into the back seat, he waited, a firefighter on either side. Then he nodded and the firefighters boosted him into the front next to the pilot, who greeted him warmly. Once he was secured in his seat, they closed the door.

After a few moments, the pilot tipped his side window open and called out "Clear!" There was a pop-pop sound and then a whining as the propellers began turning. The engine caught and the Cessna rumbled away. Jenna and the others watched as it paused near the runway, then taxied onto it, and abruptly surged forward, rising into the air, rapidly becoming a small dot against the cloudless sky.

Two hours later, Randall and Sharon were smiling and waving from the Cessna's windows when the plane taxied back toward Jenna and the rest of the group. Hurrying to meet it, the firefighters opened the door on Randall's side and helped him into his wheelchair, and then Sharon and the pilot got out.

"When you let someone else do the flying, you sure see a lot more," Randall said to the group. Everyone laughed, and Sharon took her husband's hand, explaining they had flown over canyons, lakes, and the craggy peaks toward the north of the range.

"Randall really knows the Uintas," the pilot said, smiling. "It was a great tour for me too."

"We saw so much," Sharon said. "It was beautiful, just beautiful!"

Randall cleared his throat and said, "Sharon and I want to thank all of you for doing this for us."

In the period that followed, Randall confounded the doctors. Instead of worsening, he began to improve. After six months of care by Silverado Hospice, he no longer needed its services and was discharged. Randall was able to leave the skilled nursing facility and move back home. He lived there happily with Sharon for another year before passing away, his life complete.

Chapter Sixteen

Generations

The soul is healed by being with children.

– Fyodor Dostoyevsky

The administrator greeted the white-haired couple as they entered Silverado, and the three talked for a few moments. Then the administrator turned to Maddie, who was standing by the front desk.

"Maddie, can you please show Mrs. Sanders where her room will be?" she asked.

"Yes," Maddie said, hurrying over. "It's very pretty. I'm sure you'll like it." As she escorted the pair toward the hallway, she added, "It's on the second floor. The shower is a little hard to use, so I'll show you how it works."

When they arrived at the room, Mrs. Sanders entered first. Still in the hallway with Mr. Sanders, Maddie turned toward him and said, "When she moves in, I'll make sure she gets to know her way around. We have a tea party every afternoon, and I'll take her on her first day."

He later told Silverado's staff that Maddie's warm helpfulness reassured him that his wife was moving to the right place, that she would be happy and loved here.

Maddie was seven then.

The first time Maddie came to Silverado, she was eight months old. Her mother, Laura, pulled her across the threshold in a red wagon. In her previous employment, she had worked at a skilled nursing center, but found it difficult with a newborn baby at home. A co-worker, sympathetic to the young mother, told her she had heard Silverado was more child-friendly and suggested Laura contact the company.

At Silverado, Laura discovered a policy that shatters the norm not only in senior living but also everywhere in the business world. Silverado actually encourages its staff to bring their kids to work as often and for as long as they wish. Youngsters can have as many meals and snacks as they like at no cost to their parents.

After Laura was hired, she settled into her new position and started arriving for work each morning with her daughter in tow. The residents greeted Maddie with such joy that Laura began a daily routine of rolling her through the community. One day, a resident suggested Laura leave Maddie with her for a while. Laura hesitated, but the love on the woman's face overcame her reservations. Unseen, she checked on Maddie several times during the next hour. When she finally came back to retrieve her little girl, she found Maddie giggling in the woman's lap as four other residents played with her.

By fencing in part of Silverado's living room, Laura created a play area where residents could sit and watch Maddie, chatting among themselves. Eventually, preschool took Maddie from Silverado for three days a week, but otherwise, she could be found singing songs with residents in Music Club or helping to brush the dogs and fill their bowls. A welcome regular at the front desk, Maddie was intuitively able to put new residents and their families at ease.

Loren, Steve, and the late Jim Smith made Silverado's unique childcare policy a founding practice. They wanted to give parents of the staff peace of mind by solving the babysitting dilemma and by allowing parents to connect with their children during work hours. At Silverado, the presence of children promotes normalization; interaction with people of varying generations is part of daily life. The practice has helped Silverado attract high-quality, family-oriented employees to carry out the company's mission.

For a number of Silverado residents, involvement with children provides meaning and new energy. They look forward to getting up in the morning, a desire that may previously have been extinguished by depression or a lack of purpose. So important is the presence of youngsters that in addition to encouraging associates to bring their children to work, the company also invites schools and youth organizations such as Scout troops to come to Silverado regularly, not just to visit but to befriend and participate with residents.

A newborn slumbers quietly on the lap of a resident who possesses baby-calming secrets known only to those with years of experience. A kindergartner works on counting beyond his fingers under the tutelage of a former engineering professor. Two elementary students and a silver-haired man throw a ball for a Labrador retriever. A junior high schooler and a resident brush a final coat of varnish onto a table they built together. A high school senior planning to major in art helps lead a resident watercolor class. The generations meet at Silverado. Each teaches and learns, gives and receives, as the generations do everywhere else in the world.

On the jungle gym in Silverado's backyard, a staff member's child suddenly had an idea. "Let's paint the gym set!" he yelled excitedly. Dashing inside to the room where art supplies were kept, he brought back a handful of colored markers and offered them to his companions. The children began making bold streaks of black, red, and green on the jungle gym. When an elderly resident glanced out the window and saw what they were doing, she hurried to the office of Kathryn, the administrator, to alert her.

"How would you handle this?" Kathryn asked the resident.

"We should make them clean it," she replied in the brisk tone of one experienced at teaching right from wrong. "They need to learn to be responsible for their actions."

"Then that's what we'll do," said Kathryn, rising and gesturing for the resident to follow her to the utility room. The two women filled buckets with soapy water and grabbed fistfuls of clean rags. Walking through the community, they rounded up the now-scattered culprits and took them back outside to the jungle gym.

"You need to clean this up," the resident told the children. In awe of the calm authority of her tone, they set to the task at once. Staying to supervise until they had wiped the last marks off the equipment, Kathryn suggested that after they rinsed out the rags and stowed the buckets, the youngsters should help her raid the freezer in the country kitchen for ice cream sandwiches.

Bringing children together with the memory impaired has created the environment that Loren, Steve, and Jim envisioned – one where the memory impaired are fully accepted and empowered.

Rebecca joined Silverado's staff in 1999 and began to bring her nine-year-old daughter Jackie to work with her. Throughout her school years, Jackie arrived after classes. She would grab a snack from the country kitchen refrigerator and find a quiet place to do her homework. When she finished, she often hurried to the Culinary Club to slice and sauté alongside the members. At other times, she grabbed a watering can to participate in the Garden Club. She also helped hook up leashes and accompanied residents exercising Silverado's dogs.

Jackie says becoming part of Silverado life at such an early age taught her that people with Alzheimer's aren't scary. Seeing her mother's compassion for the residents and understanding the difference she made in their lives every day deepened Jackie's respect for her mother and forged a stronger bond between the two. It also created a resolve within Jackie to dedicate her career to improving the lives of those with memory impairment. The best way to do it, she believed, would be to work for Silverado. After she graduated, she joined the Silverado staff as a caregiver. When Jackie's daughter was born, she began bringing her to work just as her mother had done. Jackie wants her to absorb the same lessons about improving the lives of others that she did when she was a youngster.

At sixteen, Katelyn had never met a person with Alzheimer's disease. Neither had her friends, but she was more anxious than any of them. Katelyn was the reason the carload of teens was heading to Silverado that afternoon. Her mother, Ellen, had recently joined the company as a Director of Health Services and had suggested that Katelyn volunteer at the community. With butterflies in her stomach, Katelyn invited several pals to accompany her and was relieved when they agreed. They all wondered what they would encounter. Would the people there look different, say strange things, act weird?

A year later, Katelyn recalled, "The residents were all normal sweet people who were so nice. The place was warm and welcoming. When we left at the end of that day, we all wanted to come back." And they did, spending hours participating in activities with residents and helping with events around the community.

About two months later, during Katelyn's summer vacation from school, her grandmother, Mary Jane, experienced a severe health decline and moved into Silverado. Wanting to be with her grandmother as much as possible, Katelyn slept in Mary Jane's room many nights and spent almost every day at the community, leaving only for a few hours to attend a daily tennis camp. Silverado became Katelyn's community. The residents who had sparked such anxiety in her only a few months earlier turned out to be some of her closest friends.

"We would walk together and talk and they would take my mind off my grandmother's illness. We would have so much fun doing things like making cookies or telling stories. There is just something so special about the residents," she concluded.

When her grandmother passed away, her newfound friends were there to comfort her. Now, Katelyn wants to make a lasting contribution to Silverado by helping residents at the community form their own chapter of the Silverado Service Club. A longtime Girl Scout, Katelyn is setting up the project through the organization's Gold Star Award program, the highest Girl Scout honor. Passionate about the endeavor, she hopes to involve dozens of other young people.

She says, "We need to change the world's view of people with memory impairment. I understand now how capable people with Alzheimer's disease can be; they still have so much to offer the world around them."

Savannah turned on the computer in her lap and took a sip of tea from the mug on her nightstand. Closing her eyes, she leaned back against the pillows propped against the headboard of her bed. How could she hone what she wanted to say to just five hundred words? She opened her eyes, took a deep breath and fortified herself with more tea. Then she sat up and began tapping the keyboard.

"I remember sleeping on the floor under my mom's desk at night," Savannah wrote. "She was a single mom until I was about five years old, which meant I had to go to work with her at Silverado."

Silverado was a community for those with dementia, Savannah tapped on the keys. "My aunt refused to go into the building, because she was afraid of the people inside. I couldn't understand what frightened her; in my eyes, they were sweet, sometimes forgetful, old people who smiled at everything I said. Silverado was my second home."

Pausing over her computer, Savannah realized she couldn't recall a time when Silverado wasn't part of her life. She was only two years old when her mother, an aide, first brought her there. She quickly learned to emulate how her mother cared for the memory impaired. If Savannah saw a resident who seemed sad, she would put her tiny hand in his and grin up at him, invariably causing him to smile back. By kindergarten, Savannah was helping the residents with their food; at the age of seven, she could sense the needs of those who were agitated and redirect their attention to calm them.

As an elementary school student, Savannah assisted with the residents' Art Club. When she entered junior high school, her mother became a charge nurse. By observing her, Savannah learned care techniques and began to provide one-on-one attention to the residents.

Reaching for her tea and taking another sip, Savannah thought about what she wanted to say. Her eye caught the framed sketch hanging above her dresser. To a casual observer, it was just a few pencil marks. Hastily setting her mug down, Savannah resumed typing at a rapid clip.

"In the beginning, he was a fantastic artist. He did a painting of another resident that was so detailed that at first I believed it was a photograph. As his disease got worse, his portraits of the woman became less detailed, without light or shading in her eyes. As he gradually lost control of his hands, he used pencils until his last penciled sketch of the woman was barely recognizable. There was an oddly-shaped oval for a head, two dots for eyes and a line for the nose."

The artist gave Savannah that final drawing and her mother framed it for her. It had been hanging above Savannah's bureau ever since, even though she was now about to graduate from high school.

Savannah continued typing with urgency. "When I saw that sketch, I realized what was really occurring in Silverado: these people were losing themselves to a disease that was stealing their identity. The thought of becoming an empty shell of myself, unable to remember who I am, the names of my relatives, unable to even use the restroom on my own, gave me a strong sense of devastation. I wanted to know what caused these illnesses and what physical changes were occurring that allowed such a horrible diseases to exist."

Her passion, Savannah wrote, for learning about the nervous system was sparked. "I wanted to see the differences between brains with and without Alzheimer's. I wanted to know what science might be able to do to prevent and heal the disease. When I learned there was not yet a prevention or cure for that man whose hands had betrayed him, I decided what I wanted to do with my life. I would make changes in the lives of people suffering from diseases like Alzheimer's, because they are the most tragic. I know that whatever I end up doing, I want to work for real individuals, for real people, not try to solve anonymous medical cases."

Laying her hand on the mug of tea, Savannah was surprised to discover it had gone cold. A glance at the clock told her it was past midnight. She saved her work, shut the laptop off, and turned out her light.

A few months later, Savannah learned that all twelve colleges she had applied to had accepted her. She is now enrolled in the University of California, Davis, Department of Neurobiology.

Tessa slid aside the flowerpot she had decorated with blue and green stars, her small hand pausing over the sheets of stickers on the table in front of her. Selecting a set with yellow and orange birds, she began pasting them on another flowerpot. Normally a chatterbox, Tessa hadn't said a word this morning. Instead, the eight-year-old's face was furrowed with the concentration necessary to align the decorations just so. Kathy, the resident engagement director, sensed that her silence stemmed from more than just the task at hand.

Having crafts to complete was part of Silverado's monthly children's support group. Kathy started the group after noticing three youngsters who looked sad and confused when they visited their grandmother. Realizing that dementia's impact on children is often overlooked, she found that giving the kids a project to work on broke the ice, making it easier for them to talk about how they felt as memory-impairing diseases changed the lives of their grandparents and great-grandparents. The support group has flourished and has become a model throughout Silverado, with children outside the organization welcome to attend as well.

"OK, everyone," Kathy said, "Let's take a break and have something to eat." She went to the side of the room where picnic-style box lunches were stacked and brought them back to the big round table where Tessa and four other youngsters were sitting surrounded by flowerpots, stickers, and stencils.

"All right!" exclaimed Theo, Tessa's brother, older by four years. "It's the chicken salad!"

Kathy smiled. The previous month, Theo had said he wanted his mother to ask Silverado's chef for the recipe. When everyone had unwrapped the sandwiches and started to eat, Kathy knew the moment was right.

"So, how are things going?" she said in a casual tone. As she asked the question, she looked over at Theo, silently willing him to catch her eye. He met her gaze and understood the prompt.

"Well, Tessa," he said to his little sister, "it hasn't been easy for you, has it?" She looked at him and bit her lip. Realizing that she wasn't going to say anything, Theo continued, "The last couple of times we came here, Grandma called Tessa by Mom's name. She tried to explain to Grandma that her name was Tessa, but Grandma kept doing it. Tessa has been pretty upset about it."

"Oh, Tessa, I understand how you feel," Kathy said. "That must be confusing, maybe even scary."

Tessa nodded.

"But it really isn't anything to be frightened of," Kathy continued. "Remember how we talked about what happens with the memories of people with dementia? They're better at remembering things from a long time ago. So when your grandmother calls you by your mother's name, it means you remind her of your mother when she was a little girl. If she does it again, don't try to correct her. Just let her do it."

With his sister still quiet, Theo said, "Tessa, you don't need to be scared.

She's still Grandma."

"That's right," Kathy said. "She is still Grandma. Now, you know when we share our feelings in here, you don't have to worry that your grandmother will know you were upset. Just remember that she loves you and that's what matters most."

Tessa didn't say anything right away. But after she and the other youngsters finished lunch and resumed decorating the flowerpots, she began talking and laughing. The group worked diligently, knowing that Silverado's resident Garden Club needed fifteen of them by the end of the afternoon. When the kids were finished and the meeting drew to a close, Kathy gave each of them a disposable camera. She reminded the youngsters they could use the cameras to take pictures with their grandparents. Then the children could add the photos to a scrapbook kept at Silverado.

"You know you can come and get the scrapbook whenever you wish," she said. "You can show it to your grandparents and talk about the fun you've had together."

Two weeks after the discussion with Tessa and Theo, Kathy happened to come across the little girl walking down the hall with her grandmother.

"How was school, Rachel?" the older woman asked Tessa.

Without hesitating, Tessa said, "I got an A on my spelling test." Then she took her grandmother's hand and the pair headed toward the door leading to the backyard. Tessa was clutching her disposable camera in her other hand.

Loren Shook was a five-year-old child when his family moved to the grounds of a psychiatric sanitarium. At first, he was too young to comprehend why the patients were there. To him, they were like anyone else. As he grew older, he began to understand that the world did not recognize them as normal. But Loren's perception never changed. Every human being has an inner spirit. Even when it becomes obscured, we can connect with it if we try hard enough. This is as true for the memory impaired he now serves as it was for the people with mental illness he knew earlier in life.

When Loren reflects on the journey that led him to establish Silverado, he feels God called him to do this work. Two decades later, he admits he would never have disclosed this information when he was scouting investors and wrangling with paperwork in the effort to turn his dream into reality.

"I didn't say it, because I was not sure how it would be interpreted." Those closest to Loren feel his beliefs have evolved and deepened over the years because of Silverado.

His son Aaron, a teenager the year Silverado opened its doors, says, "I've watched my dad become more spiritual through this process. I think he has a much better understanding of what's important."

Heather, like Aaron, was in her teens when her father Loren took her to Silverado for the first time. He walked with her along the hallways, showing her the memory boxes and explaining why they mattered so much. Pausing in the country kitchen, he told his daughter the airy room wasn't only about food. Like the kitchen in any home, it was a place people came together. Then, spreading his arms wide, he described how residents could stroll through the community and around the grounds without locked doors blocking their way. This encouraged exercise and eased restlessness. He added that some memory-impaired people are thought to have a wandering problem; in fact, many are just frustrated at feeling confined or not having anywhere meaningful to go.

When they stepped back into the hall, a gray-haired man approached them. As he neared, Heather saw that his body was too thin to carry much muscle, but he held himself with precision and spoke with calm sobriety.

"Please," he said to Loren. "I can't find my tent and I'm wondering if you know where it is. I need to get back to my company right away."

"Yes, Sergeant Lucas, I do know where it is," Loren said to the man in a tone both somber and sincere, one that reflected the important nature of the question. "I would be happy to take you there."

Loren touched the man's back with his palm and the two went down the hallway. Young Heather realized that she was to wait for her father's return. She glanced around, and the nearest memory box caught her eye. It displayed several medals, along with black and white photos of a handsome youth in uniform, appearing just a few years older than she was at the time.

Heather leaned in to read framed newspaper clippings that were posted beside the pictures. They described military operations in France in 1943. She looked over at the nameplate on the door by the box. "Sergeant Edward Lucas." Heather turned and peered in the direction of her father and the other fellow. Her dad was crossing Silverado's back garden, taking the man to the place that mattered most in this moment. Loren was helping Sergeant Lucas find his tent.

AFTERWORD

Government officials, health care experts, and business people representing more than three dozen nations around the globe have toured Silverado communities. Executives from other memory care organizations regularly tour our communities and offices taking notes and photographs. Often, we're asked why we "give Silverado's secrets away to the competition." Our answer is simple: No one who cares about memory-impaired individuals is a rival. Rather, he or she is a welcome partner in Silverado's vision to transform the daily lives of people with Alzheimer's disease and similar conditions.

Since 1996 when we founded Silverado, much has happened. Having expanded to encompass numerous locations in multiple states, the organization now includes home care, care management, and hospice.

Silverado's academic affiliations have grown, too. The partnership of our first community with the University of California, San Diego, led to relationships with other acclaimed academic institutions. They include the University of California, Los Angeles; University of California, Irvine; University of California, San Francisco; University of Southern California; Stanford University; University of North Texas; Baylor College of Medicine; the University of Utah, and many others. Through these affiliations, Silverado's staff and residents serve as invaluable resources in research, teaching, and care practices designed to better the lives of the memory impaired everywhere.

The book Alive with Alzheimer's, by Cathy Stein Greenblat, released by University of Chicago Press in 2004, has spread Silverado's message around the globe. A Professor Emerita of Sociology at Rutgers University, Greenblat spent two months at one of our communities, where she photographed and interviewed residents, their families, and our staff. Her book has been widely distributed, and her photographs of Silverado have been exhibited across the United States – including the National Institute of Health – and throughout Europe, Japan, and India. We still receive correspondence from individuals and organizations galvanized by Greenblat's portrayal of the vibrant daily life at Silverado. In addition, Silverado was featured in Greenblat's subsequent publication, Love, Loss, and Laughter: Seeing Alzheimer's Differently.

We are honored to be asked to speak regularly at regional, national, and international conferences. As we had hoped from the beginning, Silverado's practices have been reaching an ever-increasing global community of professionals and laypeople committed to improving the lives of those with memory impairment.

Silverado has been featured in online and print publications, including The Wall Street Journal, The Los Angeles Times, The Huffington Post, The Chicago Tribune and other top publications in major markets across the United States, in addition to numerous short segments appearing on morning and evening news shows in markets such as Houston, Salt Lake City, Los Angeles, Dallas, and on Good Morning America. Also, a documentary produced by Cathy Greenblat and Australian filmmaker Corinne Maunder, Love Lives Here (part of a three-part series called Side by Side: Love and Joy in Dementia Care), was used as part of an educational series by the Australian Aged Care Quality Agency. Today, elements of Silverado's model are being implemented by others, domestically and internationally. This is all very exciting to us!

There is much more to do.

Despite enormous effort by researchers, no drugs or medical procedures for preventing or curing memory-impairing diseases have yet been found. It is critical that the research continues, and Silverado supports it in every way through funding, volunteering, and willingness to share knowledge. That said, we would also like to see more resources dedicated to improving the lives of people who currently have memory impairment. We firmly believe care should be on an equal footing with cure, and that is our reason for writing this book.

Of course, dementia is not contagious, but those suffering from it in the twenty-first century are avoided like the lepers of previous centuries. It is true the behavior of the memory impaired can be frightening, and it is natural to fear illnesses that could occur in one's own future; however, it is cruel to allow this fear to define our approach to the memory impaired.

Every day, we witness the memory impaired being rejected by those around them. Many people with dementia are locked behind doors in their own homes. They don't participate in normal everyday activities because they are shunned by contemporaries who don't want to be reminded that they too may be vulnerable. Others are warehoused in facilities where few outsiders venture. In many senior living communities, residents whose memories are ebbing cease coming to the dining room – because no one will sit with them. Thus, the memory-impaired become isolated, which worsens their symptoms and negatively affects their emotional and physical health.

Reaching out to the memory impaired offers us the opportunity to act from the best part of ourselves. Take the time to visit them in a senior community or adult day center on a regular basis. Participate alongside them in activities. Talk or spend quiet moments together. Just being present for a few hours a month will have a powerful impact on a lonely soul. Talk to people in your church or nonprofit organization about getting involved. If you lead a youth group, have the youngsters take part.

Silverado has taken active steps to partner with cities we operate in – such as Azusa, California – to form dementia friendly cities. By joining the movement of dementia friendly cities, you too can make a difference in the fight and the stigma against dementia. With understanding comes acceptance.

We also encourage you to take steps to care for your own memory. Lifestyle changes, which were key to Silverado from the start –mental stimulation, physical exercise, socialization, and sound nutrition – are now widely recognized as a deterrent to memory-loss.

If there is a history of dementia in your family, take advantage of the memory screening procedures available for detecting the condition in its earliest stages. You may feel you'd rather not know the results. But by identifying dementia as early as possible, you and your doctor can develop a care regimen that might include lifestyle changes and drugs to slow the disease's progression.

Because of early detection, we have met many people who know they are in the initial stage of memory impairment. This information has enabled them to make timely choices about their finances, living arrangements, and care in the future. It also allows them to participate in the larger discussion of how society will care for the growing numbers of memory impaired.

When our residents go to an art museum, dine in a restaurant, or help run an errand to the store, they prove their rightful place in the world to all who see them. In meeting with physicians, social workers, and other health professionals in the locations we serve, we make the case for Silverado's life-affirming approach to care. By inviting the public to educational and social events at Silverado, we demonstrate the love-centered practices that are in the very best interests of the people in our care.

In all ways, we seek to raise our voices on behalf of the memory impaired. We encourage everyone who wants to learn more about dementia care or who would enjoy the pleasure of new friendships to come spend time with us. We ask for your help in bringing about a transformation.

Embrace this cause with love.

Put aside fear.

Discover that in giving of yourself, you are changed forever.

Join us as we pursue the true purpose of Silverado, to change the world in how people with memory impairment of all types are treated and how people move from this life to their next destination, always honoring their spiritual beliefs.

Loren Shook and Stephen Winner

SCENES FROM SILVERADO

We should consider every day lost on which we have not danced at least once. And we should call every truth false which was not accompanied by at least one laugh.

– Friedrich Nietzsche

Nothing describes Silverado as well as experiencing it. Come inside and take a look.

In the Gazebo

Whether Walter was in Silverado's country kitchen, the garden, his room, or elsewhere in the community, Lisa somehow always knew where to find him when she arrived after school. This was no small feat in a building of 38,000 square feet on a five-acre campus. But it was the kind of bond they had. Lisa, the seven-year-old daughter of a Silverado laundry employee, had been blind since birth. But she knew where Walter was because it was the place she would have chosen to be, too.

That afternoon, Lisa found Walter sitting in the gazebo. Walter spotted her crossing the lawn and broke into a wide grin.

"Lisa, I'm over here," he called out. He knew Lisa's instinct would bring her to him anyway, but he just felt so much pleasure in saying her name.

Lisa's face lit up and she hastened to hug him. They sat and talked for a bit. Then Walter asked the question that Lisa was expecting, the one she hoped he would ask.

"Lisa, can you count to 200 for me?"

"One, two, three," Lisa began. Walter leaned a little closer to her and listened attentively as she continued. He was committed to improving her math skills. Lisa, excellent at the subject, in truth needed no practice. But every time she reached 200 without an error, Walter would congratulate her, and the pride in his voice always made her happy.

After she finished counting and sat a while, Lisa took Walter's hand and placed it on her face and asked, "Am I beautiful?"

"You are the most beautiful little girl there ever was," Walter told her. "Your hair has a soft sheen that reflects the sun. Your complexion is the envy of little girls everywhere. Believe me, you are a gift from God." Lisa smiled and bowed her head. She felt for Walter's hand and grasped it. They were both quiet for a while.

Then, Lisa said: "I can count to 400, too."

"I would like to hear that," Walter replied.

Walter was 99. According to scientists, his advancing memory impairment by now would have reduced the size of his brain by one-third. Many scientists claim that the actions of a person in his condition are no longer guided by intention or comprehension.

But Walter knew exactly what Lisa needed. She was his purpose.

The Nurse

"How are you today? How are you feeling?"

Silverado's residents were accustomed to hearing this question from Betty every morning. If they said they felt any way other than great, Betty would furrow her brow and ask for details. She cared about their health; they knew that.

Betty was four feet and eleven inches tall, a dynamo who carried a clipboard to take notes on what the residents told her. Meeting her, you would assume she was a member of Silverado's care team. In fact, she was a retired nurse who resided at the community. Her memory impairment meant she could no longer live by herself, but it had not dampened her interest in the well-being of others. Nor had it erased the instincts she had accumulated over the decades. Silverado's staff provided her with the clipboard and welcomed what she had to say.

It was a blow to everyone at Silverado the day a seizure extinguished Betty's vitality and sent her to the hospital. Doctors placed her on a ventilator and told her family that Betty had little time left. Betty could not communicate much, but she was able to let her relatives know that she wanted to return to Silverado. It was her home. It was where she was needed.

Betty was taken back to Silverado and gently tucked into her bed. Silverado Hospice joined the team in caring for her. Along with Betty's family, Silverado staff and residents visited her constantly as she lay prone, her eyes closed. They held her hand, told her they loved her, and talked to her even though they weren't sure she understood. Caregivers styled her hair each morning and painted her nails. It didn't matter that her life was coming to its conclusion. "We want her to look her best."

Three days after Betty returned from the hospital, Silverado's administrator Carole walked into her room. She was startled to find Betty sitting up, grinning and gazing out the window, where early evening shadows were lengthening into darkness.

"Is it night already?" she asked.

"Yes, it is," said Carole. "The days certainly fly by when we're having so much fun."

Betty chuckled and blew her a kiss. A few days later, she left her bed to take part in a chair exercise program. Then she joined the community's walking group on its daily rounds, only occasionally using a walker for support.

One day, Betty was looking out one of Silverado's windows when she saw a staff member take a tumble in the garden. She came outside, clipboard in hand, as several other people were assisting the woman to her feet.

"How are you?" Betty asked, her face creased with concern. "Can I do anything to help? I'm a nurse."

"Thank you," they told her. "We feel so much better because you're here."

They were all smiling at Betty as they said that, but you didn't have to look closely to see their tears.

Love

Josephine was standing at the entrance again. She had moved into Silverado the previous week. Since then, she had spent nearly every waking minute in the community's foyer, rattling the handle of the front door and saying, "I want to leave. Please open this door. I want to leave."

All the other doors to the exterior opened with a simple push of the hand; they led onto Silverado's secure grounds, and people at the community were encouraged to go in and out as much as they liked. The main entrance, however, was locked from the inside so staff would know if residents were leaving the premises.

Josephine didn't want to do anything except jiggle that doorknob. Regardless of how many activities she was asked to join, how many potential new friends she was introduced to, she always darted back to the foyer as soon as she could.

The caregivers were perplexed. They wanted Josephine to be happy in her new home. Despite all of Silverado's years of experience in caring for the memory impaired, no one could figure out how to help her.

On a conference call, caregivers consulted with staff at other Silverado communities. They described how Josephine rattled the door handle for hours every day and how they tried to no avail to involve her in life at Silverado. When they finished talking, there was a moment of silence and then a sudden question from one of those listening –

"Have you told her that you love her?"

The caregivers gasped. No, they hadn't. Everyone had been so worried about Josephine they hadn't done this simple thing that is so important at Silverado.

From that day on, each time the staff saw Josephine, they hugged her and said, "Josephine, we love you. You're safe here."

Within three weeks, the noise of Josephine rattling the doorknob ceased. It was replaced by the sound of her laughing during the community's club activities, singing in the music groups, and talking with new friends. She realized she was safe and loved, and that had vanquished her fears.

The Inspection

Since the diagnosis of Wendell's memory impairment four years previously, his wife Joanie had been caring for him at home. She was just a little younger than her 84-year-old husband, and he now needed more assistance than she could handle. On the morning Wendell was moving into Silverado, Joanie felt the anguish and loss that often come with separating from a beloved spouse, even when there's no doubt it is for the best.

Confiding in the staff, Joanie told them she was distressed because Wendell had refused to bathe for several weeks. This man who had been so meticulous and dashing in his Coast Guard uniform when they first met at a coffee social six decades earlier was arriving at his new home unkempt. A Silverado caregiver comforted her: "This problem isn't unusual. The next time you see him, he'll be shipshape."

They helped her arrange pictures of Wendell from his Coast Guard days in the memory box outside his room. Then, Joanie told Wendell she would see him the next day and she went outside to her car.

Back inside, caregivers talked gently with Wendell about bathing. He refused. They discussed it with him delicately several more times during the afternoon and he continued to say no. As staff members shared information about the community's newest resident, employees from all departments learned of this challenge. At Silverado, everyone is considered part of the care team, regardless of his or her official title.

An hour before dinner, Jack, director of maintenance for the community, paused to study Wendell's memory box. The door to Wendell's room was open. Jack tapped on the door frame and asked for permission to come in. Wendell nodded. Jack entered and announced, "Inspection is in 20 minutes. You need to shower and shave right now so you're ready."

Wendell rose to his feet. Jack stepped back into the hall and gestured for assistance from the caregivers, who immediately came to assist Wendell.

When Joanie arrived at Silverado the following day, Wendell was waiting for her in the foyer. His hair was neatly combed, his face freshly shaved, and he emanated the pleasing scent of cologne. She reached out to hold him tight. To Joanie, Wendell didn't look any older than when they first met at that social. If anything, he seemed even more handsome.

The Dance

Dessert plates were cleared away and people sipped their last coffee. Residents left Silverado's dining room for various post-meal pursuits. A group headed to the living room, where they gathered with caregivers in an informal circle.

It had been another busy day, with many get-togethers of all kinds. Now, as dusk was softening the sky outside the picture windows, the room was quiet, but not for long. Janis, a caregiver, inserted a ragtime CD into the player and pranced her way to the center of the circle. She smiled toward Mario, the caregiver coordinator. And Mario, who had never considered himself a dancer, found himself shimmying toward her.

Janis took the hand of a graying gentleman, who stood and moved in rhythm. Soon, other pairs of staff and residents were dancing, with some caregivers stooping to partner with those in wheelchairs. When the CD finished, Mario loaded another one into the player, then another.

Had you later asked the residents for details about the evening, they probably couldn't have answered. Memory impairment ravages short-term recollection. But remembering the event isn't important. What matters is experiencing the joy.

A few days later in response to a question about his work, Mario, the caregiver coordinator, responded, "When I'm working at Silverado, I don't want to leave. And when I'm not at Silverado, I think about what might be happening here."

He fell silent, not finding the words to explain exactly why he felt that way. He didn't need to.

Have a Cup of Coffee

Max visited Jeanne every day during the seven years his wife resided at Silverado – weekdays, weekends, holidays, good and bad weather. Nothing changed Max's routine of rising from his bed in their home of several decades just after dawn and driving two and a half miles to the community to be with Jeanne. It wouldn't have occurred to him to do anything else.

"From the moment I met her, I worshiped her," Max said. Fifty-seven years after he picked Jeanne up at her house on a blind date for New Year's Eve, his voice catches when he describes how "the door opened, and there stood an angel."

When Jeanne's memory impairment led to a breakdown, it was clear she needed more assistance than Max could give. Silverado became Max's "home away from home." It was where he got his morning cup of coffee and read the newspaper, where he spent most of the day.

It was where he made new friendships, including with Angel, the chef. They forged their bond as they worked together to create tasty foods that would tempt Jeanne as her ability to chew and swallow declined.

When his wife passed away, he moved numbly through the busy days that followed: various arrangements to be made, visits by family and friends, the memorial service.

The morning after the last relative left town, Max rose at his customary time, got in the car, and headed toward Silverado. He was halfway to the community when he remembered his wife no longer lived there.

He kept driving.

Smiles and hugs welcomed him when he arrived at Silverado. Just like every other day for the past seven years, Max poured a cup of hot coffee and took a look at the newspaper. Then he walked through the community to make sure he said hello to all of the residents and staff.

He has returned to Silverado ever since, repeating this morning routine before heading out to tutor a third-grade boy at a nearby school and to do other volunteer work.

When family and friends ask Max why he keeps going to Silverado, he chuckles and replies, "They have the best coffee in town."

Then he adds: "Come with me and try a cup."

ACKNOWLEDGMENTS

To Steve Winner my friend and partner in founding and growing Silverado into what it is today. Silverado would not be what it is today without Steve!

To the Silverado Board of Directors and investors, Vance Caesar, Chris Lewis, Michelle Kelly and Scott Brinker, whose collective wisdom, guidance and support has been instrumental in shaping and forming Silverado into the company it is today.

To Vance Caesar who was there in the earliest days helping me when I was first incubating the idea of Silverado. Vance was my professional coach and we sat in his office together and formed the foundation of a company that later would be called Silverado. Vance is my life-long, trusted friend, mentor and guide – as every day is a new day on this journey full of opportunity for which I am eternally grateful.

I would like to acknowledge Chris Lewis and Pat Haden, partners in the equity firm, Riordan Lewis Haden (RLH). They didn't invest in start-up companies but agreed to meet with myself and Silverado co-founder Jim Smith to offer guidance about venture capital partners. A few months after our initial meeting, not only did they invest their money in our idea, but Chris joined our Board of Directors and has been an invaluable source of guidance and a catalyst for innovation since 1997. It has been Silverado's honor to serve Pat's mother, Helen, and his family and Chris's mother, Penny, and his family too. Today, Chris remains at RLH. Pat moved on to become the Athletic Director for University of Southern California (USC) from 2010 to 2016, and continues to serve as a leader at USC. The more recent partners of RLH are also valued colleagues.

The executive team is made up of senior executives who provide ongoing leadership to our valued associates, empowering them to excel in serving others supported by the unique Silverado culture that is grounded in our core operating philosophy of *Love is greater than fear*. The senior executive team includes Thomas Croal, Chief Financial Officer; Michelle Egerer, Senior Vice President of Community Operations; Dawn Usher, Chief

Administrative Officer; Kathy Greene, Senior Vice President of Programs and Services Integration; Kevin Gunter, Senior Vice President of Hospice and At Home; Jeff Frum, Senior Vice President of Strategic Alliances; and Kim Butrum, Senior Vice President of Clinical Services. A special thanks to retired senior leaders, Jack Peters, Senior Vice President of Operations, and Anne Ellett, Senior Vice President of Health Services.

Moving beyond the executive team, we want to thank the vice presidents and directors at Silverado for their leadership, energy and commitment. And for me, nothing is possible without my trusted and ever-energetic assistant, Dorine Sterner, who keeps me organized and maximizes my efficiency. Steve and I also want to express our deep gratitude to each of the company's vice presidents of operations and community, hospice and at home administrators for bringing the Silverado experience to life. Our administrators lead and manage the complexities of service, including staffs that often exceed 100 people serving our residents, clients and patients, and they embody our core operating philosophy, *Love is greater than fear*. We also appreciate our own Medical Directors, as well as the thousands of physicians, nurse practitioners, nurses, social workers and geriatric care professionals who work tirelessly each day throughout our country in order to make life better for our seniors.

Many people – families, staff and other professionals – over the years suggested we write a book. Writers Shannon Ingram and Audrey Knoth of Goldman & Associates Public Relations, and for this second edition Jeff Frum, Senior Vice President of Strategic Alliances; Beth Abbott, Vice President of Marketing and Communications; David Gill, Senior Director of PR and Communications; and Frédéric Tiberghien, Creative Director, assisted Steve and I in turning those suggestions into reality, and we are grateful for their unique passion. We also want to thank editor Sue Brantley for her dedication to editing this piece of work.

I appreciate my important mentors through the years, James Conte, Robert Green and my brother and sister-in-law, Larry and Jean Shook. And I give thanks to my pastor, Rick Warren, whose sermons and writings have helped in so many ways he will never know.

We have been blessed with long time friends and colleagues who support the Silverado vision of giving LIFE – David Burroughs, Bruce Glaser and Dave Lahr of Centerpointe Construction, whose expertise and dedication make often-complex renovations and construction a reality. Doug Pancake's architectural skills help us create physical plant innovations that empower our residents to experience freedom again.

One of my closest friends Arnold Whitman (Arnie) has been a great support to me over the years, championing and supporting not only Silverado but me as a person. It is through friends like Arnie, along with other friends and confidants from my G-7 men's group led by Vance Caesar: Dick Miller, Rod McDermott, Kenn McFarland and Robert Shackleton, who help keep me grounded with what's important in life – family, friends and spirituality.

We are grateful to the leaders, researchers and faculty at the many teaching and research centers that affiliate with Silverado: University of California San Diego, University of Southern California, University of California Irvine, Stanford University, University of San Francisco, University of California Los Angeles, Cleveland Clinic Lou Ruvo Center, Baylor University, Methodist Neurological Institute, University of North Texas, Banner Health and Banner Research Institute, University of Utah, Medical College of Wisconsin, Rush University, and Northwestern University. In particular, we thank Dr. Pinchas Cohen, Professor of Gerontology and Psychology at the University of Southern California, Dean, Leonard Davis School of Gerontology, Executive Director, Ethel Percy Andrus Gerontology Center, for his pioneering work and extraordinary leadership in education, developing leaders in our profession and USC's critical research in the field of Gerontology. And thanks to the Erickson School of Aging at the University of Maryland for their pioneering efforts to expand the number of leaders in our profession. Such excellent schools play an essential role in preparing our nation to serve the tidal wave of seniors coming our way by 2030.

Our partnership with the Alzheimer's Association and its many chapters has been invaluable, as well as all of the non-profit senior service organizations we work with around the country. We thank our many industry partners, especially the leadership and volunteers of Argentum, American Seniors Housing Association and the National Investment Center for the Seniors Housing and Care Industry.

Sincere thanks to the many lenders and support staff in the financial markets whose expertise and resources have helped make our services possible. To Thomas DeRosa, CEO of Welltower (HCN) for his trusted partnership, and for continuing to provide essential strategic and financial support. To George Chapman and Mike Stephen also at Welltower, for taking a risk in the beginning to see and support our vision; Red Capital; Fannie Mae; and to Don Ambrose, our trusted mortgage broker from the beginning.

Thanks to the many children of Silverado staff, families and volunteers. You brighten the days of our residents with your energy, companionship and the ways you embody purpose and hope for the future.

My faithful companion and silent partner who has always wanted to be by my side and usually is whenever I'm at Silverado's home office or in our communities and offices in Southern California is Ranger Shook, my beloved Labrador Retriever who serves as chief pet officer. Steve's beloved companion is Truffles, a chocolate Schipperke. Ranger, Truffles and their hundreds of friends, be they four-footed, feathered or swimming in our fish tanks, are invaluable servants providing comfort, companionship and helping to re-engage people in life who have been dealt a hard blow by a fate none of us want. These pets do this tirelessly and without complaint, always giving and receiving love, even when the recipient of their affection cannot speak.

To the thousands of residents, clients and patients that we have served and are serving along with the tens of thousands of family members who have put their trust in Silverado to care for their loved ones in a time of great need, we send you our most sincere love and gratitude. We're honored to serve each and every one of you. We consider serving you to be the same as caring for our mothers, fathers or spouses.

Finally, we extend heartfelt thanks to the thousands of Silverado associates and their families, for their commitment and passion to join us in our journey to change the world in the way the memory impaired are served, to give quality of life to our clients at home, our residents in communities and to our hospice patients, their families as well as to each other. Individually we can touch a few lives. Together – with *Love is greater than fear* as our guide – we can touch the world.

Loren Shook

SOURCES

Alzheimer's Association, http://www.alz.org/

Alzheimer's Disease International, http://www.worldalzreport2015.org/#home

Better Care Better Jobs, Robert Wood Johnson Foundation

Canadian Psychology, February 2001: Review of Flynn and Lemay's A Quarter-Century of Normalization and Social Role Valorization by Aldred Neufeldt

Cathy Greenblat, Professor Emeritas of Sociology, Rutgers University, Rutgers, New Jersey

Fairfax Hospital, Kirkland, Washington

Flynn, Robert J. and Lemay, Raymond A. A Quarter-Century of Normalization and Social Role Valorization. Ottawa: University of Ottawa Press, 1999

Fuchs, Elinor. Making an Exit. New York: Metropolitan Books, 2005

Joe W. Ramsdell, M.D., Professor and Division Head, General Internal Medicine at the University of California, San Diego

Lucia Dattoma, M.D., Department of Geriatric Medicine, UCLA Health

Scandinavian Journal of Disability Research, Vol. 8, No. 4. 2006: "Bengt Nirje in Memoriam," by Mårten Söder

Shenk, David. The Forgetting, Alzheimer's: Portrait of an Epidemic. New York: Doubleday, 2001

Snowdon, David, "Aging with Grace: What the Nun Study Teaches Us About Leading Longer, Healthier, and More Meaningful Lives", Bantam Books, 2002

Susan Stein Frazier, Project Guide, Green House Project

Susan Harnett, Reference Librarian, Eastern Virginia Medical School, Norfolk, Virginia

The Social Role Valorization Implementation Project

Wikipedia: "Normalization," "Wolf Wolfensberger"

SUGGESTED READING

Avadian, Brenda. Where's My Shoes?: My Father's Walk Through Alzheimer's. North Star Books, 2005

Bell, Virginia. A Dignified Life: The Best Friends Approach to Alzheimer's Care, A guide for Family Caregivers. Michigan: Eastern Michigan University, 2007

Brackey, Jolene. Creating Moments of Joy: A Journal for Caregivers, Fourth Edition. West Lafayette, Indiana: Purdue University Press, 2008

Calo-yo, Starr. Caregiving Tips A-Z: Alzheimer's & Other Dementias. Orchard Publications, 2008

Coste, Joanne Koenig. Learning to Speak Alzheimer's: A Groundbreaking Approach for Everyone Dealing with the Disease. Mariner Books, 2004

Dunn, Hank. Hard Choices for Loving People: CPR, Artificial Feeding, Comfort Care, and the Patient with a Life-Threatening Illness, Fifth Ed. A & A Publishers, 2009

Feil, Naomi. The Validation Breakthrough: Simple Techniques for Communicating with People with 'Alzheimer's-Type Dementia'. Baltimore, Maryland: Health Professions Press, 2002

Fortanasce, Vincent. The Anti-Alzheimer's Prescription: The Science-Proven Plan to Start at Any Age. New York: Gotham, 2009

Genova, Lisa. Still Alice. New York, New York: Pocket Books, 2010

Greenblat, Cathy Stein. Alive with Alzheimer's. Chicago: University Of Chicago Press, 2004

Mace, Nancy L. and Peter V. Rabins. The 36-Hour Day: A Family Guide to Caring for People with Alzheimer Disease, Other Dementias, and Memory Loss in Later Life, 4th Edition. Baltimore, Maryland: The Johns Hopkins University Press, 2006

Meyer, Charles. Surviving Death: A Practical Guide to Caring for the Dying & Bereaved. New London, Connecticut: Twenty-Third Publications, 1991

Oxford University Press. Hospice Care for Children. 2008

Richards, Tom. An Alzheimer's Surprise Party: Unveiling the Mystery, Inner Experience, and Gifts of Dementia. Interactive Media, 2009

Schaefer, Dan. How Do We Tell the Children? A Step-by-Step Guide for Helping Children Cope When Someone Dies. New York, New York: Newmarket Press, 2002

Shriver, Maria. What's Happening to Grandpa? New York, New York: Little, Brown Books for Young Readers, 2004

Smith, Patricia B. Alzheimer's for Dummies. New York: John Wiley & Sons, 2003

Strauss, Claudia J. Talking to Alzheimer's: Simple Ways to Connect When You Visit with a Family Member or Friend. Oakland, California: New Harbinger Publications, 2002

Twichell, Karen. A Caregiver's Journey: Finding Your Way. Indiana: IUniverse, 2002

Wexler, Nancy. Mama Can't Remember Anymore: Care Management of Aging Parents and Loved Ones. Wein & Wein Publishers, 1996

GLOSSARY OF TERMS

The following terminology is often used by medical professionals in discussing memory-impairing diseases and memory care. Additional glossaries offer further information on Silverado's website: silverado.com.

acetylcholine
A chemical in the brain (neurotransmitter) that appears to be involved in learning and memory. Acetylcholine is greatly diminished in the brains of people with Alzheimer's disease.

activities of daily living (often called ADLs)
Personal care activities necessary for everyday living, such as eating, bathing, grooming, dressing and using the toilet.

adjuvant therapy
Treatment provided in addition to primary treatment.

alleles
One of the different forms of a gene that can exist at a single locus (spot on a chromosome) or site.

Alzheimer's disease
A dementia characterized by progressive mental impairment and by the presence of excessive neurofibrillary tangles and senile plaques.

amyloid
A waxy translucent substance consisting of protein in combination with polysaccharides that is deposited in some animal organs and tissues under abnormal conditions (such as Alzheimer's disease).

amyloid plaque
Build up of amyloid protein and a primary hallmark of Alzheimer's disease.

amyloid precurser protein (often called APP)
A gene, when mutated, that causes an abnormal form of the amyloid protein to be produced.

agnosia

Literally a condition of not knowing: the inability to recognize sensory stimuli. Color agnosia is the inability to recognize colors. Visual agnosia is the inability to recognize objects in the presence of intact visual sensation.

agraphia

An acquired condition of impaired or absent writing ability.

akathisia

A condition of extreme motor restlessness. It is accompanied by subjective feelings of anxiety and restlessness.

akinesia

A state of lowered motor activity.

amygdala

One of the structures of the limbic system set of brain structures, important in memory and in the regulation of emotion.

anomia

Sometimes known as "dysnomia," it is a condition in which the patient has difficulty finding correct words.

aphasia

An acquired inability to use certain aspects of language. It can be either an expressive or a receptive language disorder. "Aphasia" is a very broad term that is made more useful by descriptive qualifiers indicating the type of language impairment involved.

apraxia

Impaired ability to perform previously chained skills in a continuous behavior. Construction apraxia is an impairment in reproducing patterns; it is assessed by observing drawing and drafting or by having the patient build three-dimensional objects. Ideational apraxia refers to impairment in the idea of the required behavior; it is usually assessed by asking the patient to perform several linked behaviors. Ideomotor apraxia refers to the inability to demonstrate motor behaviors that were known in the past; it is assessed by asking the patient to pantomime a task, such as using a can opener or a pair of scissors.

ataxia

Loss or failure of muscular coordination. Movement, especially gait, is clumsy and appears to be uncertain. Ataxic patients often sway while walking. Ataxia usually results from an inaccurate sense of position in the lower limbs. Difficulty with gait increases greatly when the patient is asked to walk with eyes closed.

atonia

Complete lack of muscle tone.

atrophy

Shrinkage of (brain) tissue due to loss of neuronal processes.

auditory verbal dysnomia

An aphasic deficit characterized by impairment of ability to understand the symbolic significance of verbal communication through the auditory avenue (loss of auditory-verbal comprehension).

autonomic nervous system

That part of the nervous system concerned with visceral and involuntary functions.

beta amyloid

An amyloid derived from a larger precursor protein; it is a component of the senile or neuritic plaques characteristic of Alzheimer's disease.

beta-secretase

An enzyme that catalyzes the splitting of interior peptide bonds in a protein. Beta-secretase acts by trimming off a protein protruding from a brain cell. This small snip is thought to be the first step in the buildup of microscopic balls of debris known as amyloid that are toxic to brain cells.

bradykinesia

A motor disorder, frequently seen in Parkinson's disease, which results from rigidity of muscles and which is manifested by slow finger movements and loss of fine motor skills such as writing.

cerebrovascular disease

Disease of the cerebrum and the blood vessels supplying it.

cerebrospinal

Of or relating to the brain and spinal cord or to these together with the cranial and spinal nerves that innervate voluntary muscles.

cholinesterase inhibitors

Class of drugs known to delay the breakdown of acetylcholine.

corpus callosum

The brain structure that connects the right and left hemispheres.

declarative memory

Recalling newly learned information about people, places and things.

delirium

An acute global impairment of cognitive functioning. Delirium is usually reversible and is mostly due to a medical cause.

dementia

A condition, usually chronic, of global impairment of cognition that occurs in the absence of clouded consciousness. In many cases, such as in Alzheimer's disease, the condition is progressive.

donepezil

A drug currently approved in delaying progression in Alzheimer's disease.

dopamine

A neurotransmitter that is important in reward-motivated behavior. It is the neurotransmitter deficient in those with Parkinson's disease.

dysarthria

Acquired impairment in motor aspects of speech. Dysarthric speech may sound slurred or compressed. Spastic dysarthria, associated with pseudobular palsy, is low in pitch and has a raspy sound, with poor articulation. Flaccid dsyarthria, associated with bulbar palsy, has an extremely nasal aspect to its sound. Ataxic dysarthria is associated with cerebellar palsy and produces deficits in articulation and prosody. Hypokinetic dysarthria, found with parkinsonism, results in low-volume speech and less emphasis on accented syllables; there are also articulatory initiation difficulties. Hyperkinetic dysarthria results in prosodic, phonation, and articulatory deficits; the loudness and accents of speech are uncontrolled. Many disorders present with combinations of the different types of dysarthria.

dysfluency

A disturbance of the fluency of speech.

dysphagia

Difficulty in swallowing.

dystonia

Involuntary, slow movements that tend to contort a part of the body for a period of time. Dystonic movements tend to involve large portions of the body and have a sinuous quality that, when severe, resembles writhing.

early onset dementia (Presenile Dementia)

Severe deterioration of mental functions before the age of 65.

fronto-temporal dementia

This term covers a range of conditions, including Pick's disease, frontal-lobe degeneration and dementia associated with motor neuron disease. All are caused by damage to the frontal lobe and/or the temporal parts of the brain, the areas responsible for behavior, emotional responses and language skills.

gamma secretase
An enzyme partly responsible for plaque buildup in the brain characteristic of Alzheimer's.

geriatric psychiatrist
A specialist in the branch of medicine concerned with both the prevention and treatment of mental illness in older people.

hippocampus
An area buried deep in the forebrain that helps regulate emotion and memory.

hydrocephalus
Abnormal accumulation of cerebrospinal fluid within the cranium, producing enlarged ventricles and compression of neural tissue.

Korsakoff's syndrome
Deterioration of the brain and cognitive abilities (particularly memory) caused by chronic and severe alcohol abuse and resulting thiamine deficiency.

Lewy Body dementia
Lewy Body dementia (LBD) is characterized by distinct cognitive impairment with fluctuating confusion, disturbance of consciousness, visual hallucinations, delusions, falls, and significant parkinsonism. Lewy bodies are abnormal proteins that occur in both LBD and Parkinson's disease. In LBD, they occur throughout the brain, including the cerebral cortex.

mild cognitive impairment (often called MCI)
A syndrome of memory impairment that does not significantly affect daily activities and is not accompanied by declines in overall cognitive function.

micrographia
Writing with very minute letters or only on a small portion of a page. Sometimes seen in patients with Parkinson's disease.

neurodegenerative
Relating to or characterized by degeneration of nervous tissue.

neuroleptics
Another term for antipsychotic medication.

neuropsychiatrist
A specialist in the medicine concerned with both neurology and psychiatry.

neuropsychological
Concerned with the integration of psychological observations on behavior and the mind with neurological observations on the brain and nervous system.

neuropsychologist
A psychologist who has completed special training in the neurobiological causes of brain disorders, and who specializes in diagnosing and treating these illnesses using a predominantly medical (as opposed to psychoanalytical) approach.

non-pharmacological
Various strategies aimed at managing problematic behaviors, including therapy, changes in the home or environment and the use of appropriate communication techniques.

nystagmus
A spasmodic movement of the eyes, either rotary or side-to-side.

paraphasia
A disturbance in the verbal output of a patient. A literal paraphasia involves the substitution of letters in a word, for example, "ridilicous" for "ridiculous." Semantic or verbal paraphrasia involves the substitution of one word for another. The two words are usually in the same semantic class: for example, "shirt" for "pants."

paranoid delusion
An abnormal mental state characterized by suspiciousness and/or persecutory trends.

parathesia
Abnormalities of sensation, especially tactile and somesthetic sensation.

Parkinson's disease
A disorder that primarily affects the motor functions of the cerebellum. Parkinson's disease is characterized by tremors and gait disturbances.

PET
Stands for positron emission tomography, which is a highly specialized imaging technique using short-lived radioactive substances. This technique produces three-dimensional colored images.

Pick's disease
A form of dementia that affects the frontal and temporal lobes and that is characterized by early loss of social grace and inhibition.

plaque
A localized abnormal patch on a body part or surface.

pseudodementia
Any form of apparent cognitive impairment that mimics dementia. A common form is pseudodementia secondary to depression.

senile dementia
Severe deterioration of mental functions in persons over age 65.

senile plaques
Areas of incomplete necrosis found in persons with primary neuronal degenerative diseases of the brain. Senile plaques can also be found, in the absence of overt pathology, in most elderly people.

synapse

The space between the terminal end of an axon and another cell body. Neurotransmitters are released in the synapse and carry signals from one nerve cell to another.

transient ischemic attacks (often called TIA's)

Brief episodes of insufficient blood supply to selected portions of the brain.

ventricles

The spaces within the brain through which cerebrospinal fluid circulates.

Wernicke's aphasia

An acquired inability to communicate verbally because of impairment of receptive abilities. Associated with lesions in the posterior portion of the dominant hemisphere.

RESOURCES

Silverado
6400 Oak Canyon, Suite 200
Irvine, CA 92618
Phone: 949-240-7200 or 888-328-5400
Website: silverado.com

Administration on Aging
One Massachusetts Avenue NW Washington, DC 20001
Phone: 202-619-0724
Website: www.aoa.gov/AoARoot/Index.aspx

Alzheimer's Association
225 N. Michigan Ave., Fl. 17 Chicago, IL 60601
24/7 Helpline: 1-800-272-3900 Website: www.alz.org

Argentum
1650 King St., Suite 602
Alexandria, VA 22314
Phone: 703-894-1805
Website: www.argentum.org

National Association of Professional Geriatric Care Managers
3275 West Ina Road, Suite 130
Tucson, AZ 85741
Phone: 520-881-8008
Website: www.caremanager.org

National Family Caregivers Association
10400 Connecticut Ave., Suite 500 Kensington, MD 20895
Phone: 301-942-6430
Website: www.nfcacares.org

National Senior Living Providers Network
Phone (NSLPN Career Network): 407-705-3056 ext. 301
Website: nslpn.com

RESEARCH AFFILIATIONS

Banner Sun Health Research Institute Banner Health
10515 W. Santa Fe Drive
Sun City, AZ 85351
Phone: 623-832-6500
Website: www.bannerhealth.com

Banner Alzheimer's Institute Banner Health
901 E Willetta St.
Phoenix, AZ 85006
Phone: 602-839-6900
Website: www.banneralz.org

Baylor College of Medicine One Baylor Plaza
Houston, TX 77030
Phone: 713-798-4951
Website: www.bcm.edu

Cleveland Clinic
Lou Ruvo Center for Brain Health
888 West Bonneville Ave.
Las Vegas, Nevada 89106
Phone: 702-483-6000
Website:
my.clevelandclinic.org/neurological_institute/lou-ruvo-brain-health

Houston Methodist Neurological Institute
6565 Fannin St.
Houston, TX 77030
Phone: 713-790-3311
Website: www.houstonmethodist.org

Medical College of Wisconsin
Department of Neurology
Dementia Research Center
9200 W. Wisconsin Ave. Milwaukee, WI 53226
Phone: 414-805-5235
Website: www.mcw.edu/neurology

Northwestern University Feinberg School of Medicine
Cognitive Neurology and Alzheimer's Disease Center
420 East Superior St.
Chicago, IL 60611
Phone: 312-503-8194
Website: www.feinberg.northwestern.edu

Rush University
The Neuroscience Institute at Rush University Medical Center
1653 W. Congress Parkway
Chicago, IL 60612
Phone: 312-942-5000
Website: www.rush.edu/

University of California Irvine (School of Medicine)
1001 Health Sciences Rd.
Irvine, CA 92697
Phone: 949-824-5926
Website: www.som.uci.edu

University of California Los Angeles (Alzheimer's Disease Center)
10911 Weyburn Ave., Ste. 200
Los Angeles, CA 90095
Phone: 310-794-2553
Website: www.eastonad.ucla.edu

University of California San Diego
(Shiley Marcos Alzheimer's Disease Research Center)
8950 Villa La Jolla Dr., Suite C129
La Jolla, CA 92037
Phone: 858-622-5800
Website: adrc.ucsd.edu/index.html

University of North Texas
1155 Union Cir.
Denton, TX 76203 Phone: 940-565-2000
Website: www.unt.edu

University of Utah
Department of Educational Psychology
1705 Campus Center Dr., Room 327
Salt Lake City, UT 84112
Phone: 801-581-7148
Website: www.ed.utah.edu/EDPS

USC Davis School of Gerontology
3715 McClintock Ave.
Los Angeles, CA 90089
Phone: 213-740-6060
Website: www.usc.edu/dept/gero

We hope you enjoyed this book from AJC Press.

If you would like to receive more information about AJC Press and our products, please contact:

AJC Press
6400 Oak Canyon, Suite 200
Irvine, CA 92618